KT-528-600

CATAPULT

An Anthology of New Writing

CHARTERHOUSE
LIBRARY
WITHDRAWN

INTRODUCED BY ANDREW MOTION

Published by the Centre for Creative and Performing Arts,
the University of East Anglia.
Typeset in Plantin Light.
Printed by Biddles Ltd.
1997 copyright reserved by individual authors.
All rights reserved.

No part of this publication may be reproduced, stored in
a retrieval system, or transmitted in any form, by any means,
electronic, mechanical, photocopying, recording or otherwise,
without prior permission from the authors.

British Library Cataloguing in Publication Data.
A catalogue record for this book is available
from the British Library.
ISBN 0 9515009 8 8

All stories are works of fiction. Any resemblance to persons
living or dead is purely coincidental.

Contents

ANDREW MOTION
   Introduction   **1**

ANDREW BRYANT
   Skylight   **5**

JOSEPHINE CORCORAN
   Four Episodes in the Life of Jocasta, Queen of Thebes   **19**

HELEN CROSS
   Rose Meets a Man   **33**

ANNA GARRY
   Extract from A Gift of Stones   **49**

AMY HOSKIN
   Extract from Mercy; Me   **69**

HAYA HUSSEINI
   Notes on Jerusalem   **87**

CHRISTOPHER JAMES
   Ten Poems   **99**

ANNETTE KOBAK
Extract from The Protectorate   113

CLAYTON LISTER
The Call   131

ESTHER MORGAN
Ten Poems   141

HELEN OSWALD
Ten Poems   161

SCOTT PERRY
Stomach   177

CHRISTINE POUNTNEY
Extract from Last Chance Texaco   197

CHARLOTTE PRICE
I Am Scrawny, I Am Young, I Will Wear My Jeans
Low-Slung   215

CAROL RAY
Dry Sherry   231

SHELLEY SILAS
Next Year in Jerusalem   243

BEN TEASDALE
Extract from 47 4F 44   257

MARK TILTON
Comedian   275

CHARLIE WATSON
Lapsang Souchong   285

MIRANDA YATES
The Regurgitator   303

Acknowledgements

Many thanks to Julia Bell, Jon Cook, Andrew Motion, Mike Oakes, Phoebe Phillips, Anastacia Tohill, Andy Vargo and Vicky Winteringham.

Special thanks to Eva Hoffman, Russell Celyn Jones, Rob Ritchie, Peter Thomson and Hugo Williams.

Catapult gratefully acknowledges support from the CCPA, and the Norwich School of Art and Design.

Catapult team: Haya Husseini
                      Clayton Lister
                      Esther Morgan
                      Charlie Watson

Cover design: Daren Mason and Quy Sam

Lyric from Don McLean's *American Pie* in Esther Morgan's *Ten Poems* Copyright © 1971, 1972, Mayday Music/Benny Bird Music/MCA Music Publishing, a division of Universal Studios Inc.

Epigraph for Shelley Silas' *Next Year in Jerusalem* taken from Tennessee Williams' *A Streetcar Named Desire*. Copyright © 1947, 1953 by Tennessee Williams, renewed 1975, 1981 The University of the South. Published by New Directions. Reprinted by permission of The University of the South, Sewanee, Tennessee.

Introduction

This is the latest in a series edited and designed by members of the Creative Writing MA group at the University of East Anglia, and published by them through the university's Centre for Creative and Performing Arts. It contains work they have written during the first two-thirds of the year-long course. In all these respects, the anthology resembles its predecessors — but this year there is an important development. For the first time since it began twenty-seven years ago, the Creative Writing MA now offers a poetry course as well as a prose one — and some of the work produced on this new course appears in the following pages.

The purpose of the anthology is to introduce the work of course members to a wider audience than can easily be found within the university. Like its predecessors, *Catapult* has a wonderful diversity of talent, while at the same time proving a shared devotion to large imaginative ambitions. Also like its predecessors, it indicates that those taking the MA course are not trying to discover whether they are writers or not. Rather, they are writers already launching into their writing lives. This is why the anthology makes such exciting reading. It introduces us to fresh voices while also showing us sure touches; it is sharp with new angles on experience, but also brimming with confidence and commitment.

ANDREW MOTION
Spring 1997

The Skylight

ANDREW BRYANT

Andrew Bryant is twenty-five and lives in Norfolk. In 1995 he graduated from Norwich School of Art and Design with a degree in Cultural Studies, and he would like to dedicate this story to George Szirtes and Peter Scupham, creative writing tutors on that course.

He normally enjoyed his sleep, for the simple reason that sleeping provided a diversion from the hours of waiting. He was waiting to hear about some jobs he had applied for. His days were spent on the sofa, anticipating a phone call, or a knock at the door, or a letter through the letter-box.

He slept with his arm across her waist. She could only get to sleep if this was done. He always slept heavily and couldn't normally be roused. She said he looked calm in his sleep, at peace with everything, and if she woke before him she liked to lean on her elbow and just watch his face.

But lately he had been having dreams, and they were interrupting his sleep. He slept for a few hours at a time, then he would wake up with a start and sometimes remain awake for another few hours. In this time, while she slept with the covers knotted around her, he would attempt to analyse what he could remember of the dreams. He could not recall ever having had such strange dreams, or so many. Each time he woke up he had this inexplicable feeling that something was about to change. Somehow the dreams suggested this. Then it would pass and he might be able to sleep again.

One Sunday he woke at eleven to find the duvet on the floor and his pillow on her back. She was on her front, her face buried in the sheets. He had woken up from a dream in which an old school friend — someone he hadn't seen in over seven years — gave him a kidnap holiday as a birthday present. In the dream, kidnap holidays were set to take off. The holiday entailed him being led into a forest and into a dark room, like a hangar he thought, where he was bound and gagged. He was then given a thorough beating by two men he

5

thought he might have recognised. The friend who had paid for this holiday turned up halfway through to see how he was getting on, whether he was enjoying himself, then joined in with the beating himself. The next minute he was on a roller-coaster, and the next he was awake staring up at the ceiling.

He called her name and she stirred. In silence they began waking up.

"You OK?" she said after a while. "Where's the covers? What's happened here?"

"I'm OK," he said. He rubbed at his eyes and tried stretching his arms. "I don't know, it's these dreams," he said. "I just had another one. I was right in the middle of it. I woke up from it just now."

"Sure you're all right?" she said. She leaned over and looked into his eyes.

"I don't feel so good. I feel tired and I ache all over. I didn't sleep too well, that's what it is," he said. He tried moving his legs and found he could only do it with difficulty.

"Your eyes are bloodshot," she said.

"They are? What does that mean?" he said.

She sat up slowly, set the pillow against the wall and leaned back. He edged over, put his head in her lap and closed his eyes. The covers stayed on the floor. It was hot, had been for weeks, and even with all the windows in the flat open the air was still.

"I had a dream too. I dreamed about a boat in a lake, a lake surrounded by blue mountains," she said. "Like Lake Tahoe? We were in a small wooden rowing-boat and we had an oar each. You dropped your oar into the water. We watched it sink. The water was clear; I could see the oar go right the way down. It kept on going but I never lost sight of it. For some reason I didn't mind that the oar was sinking. We had one oar left and we kept going round in circles. We both said we should try and make it to the shore, but for some reason we just kept going round."

He was in all her dreams; she said it made her feel secure. She was able to summon him into her dreams if things were going badly. He could not understand this, because when he dreamed he felt he was never in control of his actions. She said it took practice, but he did not believe it was possible.

"You had another dream? Tell me about your dream," she said.

She ran her fingers through her hair then held his face in her hands.

He cleared his throat, which suddenly felt dry and rough. "Well, at first I was in the house, the house with all the rooms and corridors," he said.

"The same house as in all the other dreams?" she said.

"Yes, it was. I'm sure it was," he said. "But I wasn't there for long. I don't remember much of that bit now. I just remember being frightened, like I always am when I'm in that house."

He rubbed absently at a thunder fly on his cheek. He moved his arms and legs again. Everything ached and his head felt thick. He never used to feel like this when he woke up in the mornings.

"Go on," she said. "Tell me the rest."

"Well, I remember being on a roller-coaster. It was at the Olympics, and this roller-coaster was right there in the middle of the stadium," he went on. "I can explain that bit, I think. I was awake last night. I woke up again, about two, so I put the TV on for a while. The Olympics were on so I watched some of it. Michael Johnson's broken the world record. He really smashed it."

He rolled over and lay on his back, trying to remember if that was last night or the night before. "But the rest I can't explain. It's like, I don't know, everything's mixed up. I wake up and I can't remember anything," he said.

They stayed there for a while, then she crawled out of bed. She pulled a T-shirt on and went to the door.

"You want coffee? I'm making some coffee. I think I need coffee or something," she said.

"Coffee? I don't think so," he said.

She went into the living-room/kitchen. He heard her in there, rinsing mugs, opening cupboards. It sounded muffled and distant. He put a hand to his right ear and found it was painful to touch. Even the ear lobe hurt. He heard the fridge door open.

"There's no milk," he heard her say. Her voice sounded like it was coming from under water. He heard the fridge door swinging. "No milk?" he said after a while.

She came to the door. "Do you want some breakfast? I can make an omelette. We have some eggs," she said. "I think we should eat something. I think we'll feel *better* if we eat something."

"I don't think so, I don't think I could," he said. "I think I might

be coming down with something, I really do. I feel so *tired*.
Everything aches. My *ears* hurt." He put a finger in his ear and
grimaced.

She put her head to one side and smiled at him. Then she
shrugged her shoulders and went out of the doorway.

"I think you'll feel better soon. I think it's just the heat," he heard
her say from the other room.

"Eat? I don't think so," he said.

She made black coffee for herself and brought him a glass of
water. He drank it and pulled a face. He put a hand to his throat. He
felt his neck. He thought his glands might be up.

"I don't feel good, I really don't," he said.

She began dressing. She pulled her dress on and arranged it on
her shoulders. She put her watch and necklace on while sitting at the
end of the bed.

He watched her with his head to one side. He leaned it on the
bed. He found he couldn't lift his head up for any length of time
without his neck aching.

"Don't look at me that way," she said. "I'll shower later. I don't
know, I just don't think I can be bothered at the moment."

She put her hair up and dragged her shoes over. She put one shoe
on, laboriously, then stopped. She looked at him.

"What day is it?" she said.

"It's Sunday. I think it's Sunday," he said.

She put her other shoe on and stood up. She stood in the doorway. "I have to get milk," she said. He thought she looked tired. She
never used to look this tired. She used to shower before anything
else. It was possible they were both coming down with something.

The last time either of them had left the flat was Friday. But now
the milk had run out. She had to go outside for more milk.

She looked down at him. He lay on the bed with one arm
hanging over the side.

"Baby, this can't go on," she said.

At one thirty he got up and found he was hungry. He had slept
again and dreamed about violence. He woke up with a start, his face
and hair damp. His stomach was in knots and his mouth felt numb.
She was on the sofa in the next room, asleep.

His appetite was a good sign. It came on after ten minutes of being awake. But after a few minutes of walking around in his boxer shorts he developed a headache and his limbs began to ache. There was a whistling sound coming from somewhere inside his head, which he had not noticed before.

"I don't like this, I don't like it at all," he said. "Where is this heat coming from?" She didn't stir so he shook her gently until she opened her eyes. "Where is this heat *from*?" he asked.

She watched him return to the bedroom where he collapsed on the bed with an arm over his eyes.

After a while she came in and lay next to him. She put a hand on his shoulder and brought her knees up so she fitted his shape, so she was pressed against him.

"It's cooler outside. It's lovely outside. When I came in I fell asleep again, but I've woken up and I feel *better*," she said. "I think we should go for a walk. Can we go for a walk? You'll feel better for a walk, I know it. I feel better, I really do."

He put a hand on his forehead. "I don't know, I really don't. I feel like I need to sleep some more. It's these *dreams*," he said. "I keep waking up from them. I think I just need sleep, then maybe all this will pass."

"Can we go for a walk?" she said after a while. "I'm hungry, can't we go somewhere and eat? We could sit in the park. We could do anything. You can sleep later. You have to take me outside."

"I don't know, I suppose we could," he said.

"You know what I want? Do you know what I really want?" she said. She tugged at his shoulder until he lifted his head. She ran her fingers through his hair, then she kissed the back of his neck. "I want *ice-cream*, I think that's what I want. I want to sit in the shade, by the river, with an ice-cream. Do you remember, last summer, we went to that old stately home? In the country? And there was this big lake in the grounds out the back? Do you remember?"

He scratched at his cheek. "Last summer? I don't know, it seems like years ago," he said.

"You must remember it, there were men fishing all along the banks of this lake? And this one man, he caught this fish, a fish as long as his *arm*? And everyone came and looked at it? And we sat in the shade under that tree, near those bales of straw, watching this man fishing? Only he never caught any more fish, so he laid back on the grass with his hat over his face? And we laid back too, just watching the clouds? Well, do you *remember* it?"

"I can't think. I want to remember but my head feels *thick*. What does it mean if your head feels too heavy to move?" he said. "I think I just need sleep. I don't think I can do anything until all this has passed. I have to fight this somehow."

He put his head down again and closed his eyes.

"Don't do this, don't just lay there like that," she said. She shook his shoulder. "Hey? Come *on*, I meant it now. It's all going past us, everything is. We never used to be like this. You used to take me out on Sundays. It is Sunday, isn't it? We used to have picnics by the cathedral. You used to take me to the coast, and we used to play crazy golf and make sandcastles. *Kids'* stuff, for God's sake. What happened to all the kids' stuff? Come on, what happened to all that? We used to have friends, didn't we? What happened to all our friends, to *my* friends? God, why is it I feel so *alone*?"

He rolled over then and kissed her. He kissed her hard, holding the back of her neck tight. He felt dizzy and he closed his eyes for a second.

"Let's take a walk, let's do that then," he said. "I mean it, you're right. Maybe it's the best thing to do. I don't know, I just have to fight this, that's all. I feel so *weak*, though."

"I do *too*," she said. "Don't you see? It's this heat, that's all. It's taken all your energy. But you wait, when you get outside you'll feel different. You'll see what I mean."

"I have to do something," he said. He pulled his pillow up and leaned back with his head slightly raised. "It's in my arms now," he said. He held his arms out in front of him. "It was in my head before, in my *eyes*. It's moving around, you know the way flu does sometimes?"

She said, "We can go down by the river. There's other people down there. They're renting out canoes. I saw two kids having a water fight. It's *cooler* by the river."

"When I stood up earlier I thought my legs were going to collapse under me," he said.

"We'll have a picnic," she said. "We've got bread, and there's tomatoes and cheese. We've got eggs too, I can boil them. We've got potato salad left over and there's some crisps and biscuits we didn't finish last night. We've got enough."

"I'm not sure I can eat all that much. We'll see how it goes," he said.

She smiled and kissed his cheek then his shoulder. "Will you help me? Come on, let's do this together," she said.

"All right, give me a few minutes."

She got up and went through the door. She hummed a song, an old hymn she remembered from school. She switched the TV on. She splashed water over her neck and face. Standing at the window she could hear the sound of laughter from the people by the river.

He sat on the edge of the bed and put his hands up to his head. He felt sick in his stomach. He held his shaking hands out and stared at them.

She took the cheese from the fridge and grated some into a bowl. She sliced the tomatoes and put the slices and some lettuce and chopped spring onions into a plastic container. As she did this she was boiling the eggs on the stove. She sliced some bread and buttered it. Then she remembered he didn't eat butter and she smiled to herself. She turned the sound down on the TV and stood still, listening. She went to the bedroom door.

He was on his back with his arms out, as if crucified. His jaw was set and his breathing heavy.

She watched him. She tried to work out if she had ever really felt hungry at all. She didn't feel hungry now. She didn't feel anything. She stood at the door wondering what she was supposed to do next.

He slept through until midnight. He woke two times, at six and eight-thirty, but would not remember it later. Both times she put down her book, held his arm and said his name.

She read from the Sunday papers and tried to get into one of the novels he was always reading. She watched TV, the Sunday evening programmes she hated, while laying on the bed next to him with the door wedged open. She ate the food she had prepared then took a long shower. When it began to get dark she switched off the lamp and undressed quietly. She thought she might be tired but she couldn't be sure. She got into bed and ran her fingers over his back as he slept. She concentrated on his breathing. She thought about

Sundays — Sundays in general and this day in particular. She remembered buying the milk from the corner store and watching the ducks from the bridge. She had watched the families on the bank of the river and the sun had hurt her eyes. Back at the flat, she had fallen asleep on the sofa almost immediately without really wanting to. She had boiled the kettle beforehand. It was a kettle which had to be watched. It didn't turn itself off but kept on boiling. She had awoken briefly to see the room full of steam. She had watched, feeling the steam swirling over her face, unable to move towards it, unable to stop it boiling.

She lay on her back with her eyes closed. She wanted to sleep now. She could not remember wanting a day to come to an end as much as this.

But at midnight, as she was drifting off, he woke up with a start. Without saying anything they held each other. He held her desperately. She put her head on his chest but did not close her eyes, did not attempt to sleep again.

At four he woke again. He faced the wall, trying to work out what had woken him, and when he turned over he saw that her eyes were open.

"Can't you sleep?" he said.

"I can. I'm tired. But I don't want to, I don't want to sleep," she said.

He edged himself up and put an arm around her.

"Was it another dream?" she said.

"I don't know. I guess so. I *think* it was, but I can't remember a thing," he said. He turned his head so he was back facing the wall. He opened his eyes. He stared at the radiator on the wall, inches from his face, waiting for a sign of what came next, where the first ache would come from. He thought she had fallen asleep, but in time she half sat up too and leaned into her pillow.

"I haven't slept much, I don't know why," she said. "I've been thinking about this place, about this flat." Her voice was sharp, awake. He knew they would not sleep again this night.

"You know something? I feel OK. I don't know what it is, but I feel *better*," he said. "I feel lighter, like in my sleep all the weight on me has been lifted. My head feels clear." He turned again and faced her. "What do you make of that?" he said.

In the darkness he could see she was grinning. "Do you remember a long time ago we looked in the window of that estate agents, the one down the high street?" she said, holding his arm now. "Do you remember we did it for a laugh? We were making out to be house-hunting?"

"I remember," he said.

"Do you remember the house we found? The one we both said we fell in love with? The one that had that courtyard where we said we would grow a herb garden? If we had that place? And the wooden beams? And the open fireplace?"

"And the swimming pool, and the conservatory, and that *garden*," he said. They both sat up more.

"That's the one. And do you remember you said that when we were married we would buy that place? Do you remember you said we would be married? And do you remember that in one of the photos we saw a skylight? In the roof of one of the rooms? And we said that if we had that place we'd make sure we made that room a bedroom, with the bed right under the skylight? So we could lay on the bed and look at the stars? So we could both watch the world without ever having to get out of bed?"

"The *skylight*," he said. He held her, pushed his face into her neck. Then he leaned back so they were both staring at each other. He could see light in her eyes. They were wide and expectant.

"I've *missed* you today," she said. "Where have you been today? Where were you? I've felt so *lonely*."

"I know, I *know* it," he said. "And I'm sorry. But this thing, it's been driving me mad. I felt so ill. I felt like I was going to die. I mean it, I'm not joking now. But I've slept now and it's gone. The fever has gone. I feel *lighter*."

"It's when you don't talk to me," she said. "We don't talk like we used to. Why don't we talk anymore? I get scared. You frighten me sometimes."

"I know all that. All I can say is I feel *better* now," he said. "It's gone. I can't sleep. I couldn't sleep again if I tried."

"I don't want to sleep," she said.

"I'm awake, I think I want to get up. I want to get out of this bed."

"I want to see the sun come up. Can we go outside and see the sunrise? I haven't seen a sunrise yet, not this summer," she said.

"I have to get over all this," he said.

In silence they dressed and left the flat. They walked down to the river and joined the old tow-path. On the dark water swans slept with their heads buried, their necks doubled back in a way he didn't think was possible. They walked the length of the river until it swerved off and the path came to an end.

"What now?" he said.

"I want to see the sun come up over the city," she said.

"I've never felt like this before," he said. He picked up stones and threw them into the river. He skimmed the flat ones and lost sight of them in the darkness. He found a brick which had fallen off the old bridge and made ready to throw it in the water, hovering like one of the pitchers for the Oakland A's he was always watching on late-night TV.

"Watch this!" he shouted.

He let the brick go and the splash sent ducks off the water and into the trees.

"We're wasting time, the sun's coming," she said.

They helped each other up the hill. The slope was grassy and damp. They linked arms and pulled. At the top they found the bench which looked over the city.

"All of this, so close to the flat. Yet we never come up here. Why don't we ever come up here?" she said.

They sat on the bench and he zipped his coat up to the top. The first bands of light appeared over the hospital. She smoked several cigarettes as the thin clouds were burned away. He saw she was smiling. He felt a chill in his side, but somehow the chill didn't matter.

At first it was a strip of blue which spread as the clouds dispersed. As the sun neared the surface the horizon turned pink, then a fiery orange that stabbed behind his eyes. They stood up when the sun broke over the hospital roof. They stood apart and followed it silently as it rose in line with the cathedral spire.

With the sun came the city; the shapes of offices, houses and gas tanks, the first cars, the people. They both knew the sunrise would soon end and the day would begin. They knew of this inevitability, but it didn't stop them feeling afraid.

They had come to see the sunrise and now the sunrise was gone.
She turned and faced him.
"So what happens now?" she said.
He took her hand.

Four Episodes in the Life of Jocasta, Queen of Thebes

JOSEPHINE CORCORAN

Josephine Corcoran was a winner in the 1996 Ian St. James Awards for Short Fiction and is currently working on a novel, provisionally called Freud's Maid. *She gratefully acknowledges financial support from the British Academy for her M.A. and would like to dedicate her work in this anthology to Elizabeth Galbraith and Patricia Halabi.*

Writer's note: In Greek mythology, Jocasta is the wife of Laius, King of Thebes. An oracle predicts that their baby son will kill its father and marry its mother. Fearful of this, Laius pierces the baby's feet with a spike and abandons him to die on a mountain. However, the baby is rescued by a shepherd, who takes him to the King and Queen of Corinth, where he grows up believing he is their son. He is named Oedipus, meaning 'swollen feet'. In young adulthood, Oedipus learns of the oracle's prophecy, and flees Corinth, hoping to escape his fate. While travelling, he argues violently with an older man. A vicious fight ensues and Oedipus kills him. Without realising it, he has killed his father, Laius. Oedipus settles in Thebes, where, after solving the riddle of the Sphinx, he is made King, and marries the Royal Widow, Jocasta. When it is revealed that the oracle's prophecy has come true, Jocasta hangs herself, and Oedipus blinds himself with her brooch pins.

1. *An Early Episode*

I heard my father say, "He's *very* old."

I heard my mother say, "He's very *rich*."

I heard my father say, "She is so very *young*."

I heard my mother say, "Her breasts are very big."

"He likes big breasts," my father said, "but they say he goes with herdsmen."

"He always uses goat's milk, after," my mother said. "I've heard he's very clean."

My nurse called me then, to hold her wool. When the young

soldiers went by she told me to push my bosom out, but bend my head. She told me to look at them from under my lashes.

She crushed lavender in olive oil and massaged my feet.

"This is where they like it," she said. "And they *love* it here." The bones in my feet crackled. "Now you try," she said. "Imagine I'm in uniform with my weapon strapped tightly to my hips . . . ooh, yes, Jocasta, yes . . . more pressure with your fingers, yes."

The next morning, Father came in while I was bathing. He told the girl to leave and sponged my back himself.

"Your spine is like an instrument," he said, as he held the sponge against my neck and squeezed. In the courtyard, I heard horses.

"It's early for visitors," I said.

My father said, "Wear your white dress and tell your nurse to fasten it tight."

It was an awfully long morning. My uncle was there, and my father's sister, and my older brother, Creon. They paid great attention to everything our visitor said. When they laughed at his jokes, I thought of panting dogs. He said nothing to me. His garments were purple and he smelled of jatamansi. The boys he brought with him stood up straight behind his chair. Their tunics were exceedingly short. Every now and then he rolled a growl around his throat and one of the boys rushed forwards with a silver dish. The globules hit the dish like olives. His hair melted over his shoulders; it was the colour of snow, and there were pieces of straw caught up in his beard.

"Will you sit *still!*" my mother hissed, like a bad-tempered swan. "And sit up!"

Swans are graceful, my nurse told me. She showed me how to hold my neck, straight and still, and glide.

She came for me at noon and made an enormous bow. She led me away by the hand, like she had done when I was a baby.

"I've already bathed," I told her, but she laughed and kissed my cheek. She put rose petals in the water and stood to one side, holding my robes when the others came in. She bowed again, even lower. He stood over me, looking down. The smell of jatamansi was very strong. The others clustered together, watching him, saying nothing. Not knowing what else to do, I stood up, gave him my sponge and offered him my back. He dropped the sopping sponge in a wet explosion by his feet and ran his hand down my spine, fingering each rounded note.

I heard my mother say, "His manners are appalling."

My father said, "Did you see the thickness of his golden bracelets?"

My mother said, "I thought I could smell urine, when he stood very close."

I heard my father say, "He is sending his lawyers, and his physician, to us, within the week."

They wanted me to lie still and stay indoors for the next few days. I had to sit in ass's milk for one hour every morning. I caught a chill and my father slapped my nurse.

"Didn't I tell you to warm it first?" he shouted but I'm sure he didn't, actually. The whole house seemed cloudy with bad moods, but when the physician came, my chill had gone.

"She has always been healthy, as a rule," my mother told him, and I thought that she'd rubbed a little more cochineal than usual on her cheeks.

The physician's hands were slightly damp and hot. I didn't like the way he licked his fingers or the way he asked me, "Does that hurt? Or that?"

The lawyers were more jovial. Two of them came and my father gave them rum. The rest of us went to bed and I fell asleep to the sound of booming laughter and play-fighting. When my father woke me, I had to shade my eyes from the glare of the moon. The three of them sat on my bed and one of the lawyers unrolled the largest piece of papyrus I'd ever seen, gilded with huge curls of gold leaf. He rolled my thumb in lampblack and pressed it to three places on the papyrus. Then they kissed each other and stayed a few moments, hugging, on my bed. When they'd gone I felt a slight scratch of fallen gold leaf, inside my tangled sheets.

★

Those were the last days in my parents' house.

"Time passes like clouds flying in the sky." That is what I was thinking on my wedding day, after they'd lifted off my head-dress, and I'd dropped my head backwards with relief. Fleecy clouds floated above me, untethered and free. I envied their weightlessness and thought that they were passing over me for the first and last time in my life.

The tables were laid out under the trees, almost listing under the weight of meat. Servants chased the flies away. I couldn't see any of my family in the sea of faces. A choir of boys in feather skirts shimmied around the tables, singing. The men at Laius' table showered them with rice and nuts and obscene comments. The woman sitting next to me smelt heavily of cloves and spoke a language I couldn't understand. She kept pressing my goblet to my lips and filling it with wine. The silver knocked against my teeth. Laius' table told filthy jokes. I grew drowsier and drowsier and when I closed my eyes, I saw fishes swimming, many different colours. As I slid beneath the table there was a roar of shouting like a sudden wind. The men at Laius' table waved their goblets wildly, spilling wine, and stains spread across the table linen like the livid marks of birth. The clouds swayed as I was carried to my husband's chambers.

I dreamt only of blackness until he lifted me from his bed. His eyes were red and he reeked of ouzo. I was still in my bridal gown but naked underneath and the terracotta floor was cool. Moonshine washed the room lavender-blue. I saw his toenails, long and yellow, and as he leant across the bed, his nightshirt rode up his thin, bare legs and I saw the skin around his knees, as droopy as rained-on flowers. I shivered when he drew the knife, but he sliced his fingers without any hesitation and stood like a puppet-master with invisible strings, shaking blood across the sheet. He saw me staring and said, "I'm done in, Jocasta, my child-bride."

Like a sailor pulling rope he heaved the sheet across the bed and threw it outside the door. Then he carried me into another room, wrapped me to him in the bed, and fell asleep. His chest was a breathing pillow beneath my head.

It wasn't long before the cockerels cleared their throats and I heard servants whispering and the padding of bare, busy feet. Then I heard the crowd cheering as the sheet was flown, a blood-stained flag, from the royal, gilded balcony. Laius yelled for the chamberpot and I lay there thinking that my wedding night was over.

2. *A Short Episode Involving Plums*

When my mother came to visit I complained to her, "Mother, he doesn't wash!"

"Well," she said, "you've got a tongue in your head, haven't you?"

"But when I asked him, Mother, he said, "Why should I wash it, when you're here to lick it for me?"

The water-bearer coughed.

"Yes, well, men," said Mother. "They like their little jokes."

Later, we walked in the fruit gardens, arm in arm. Four servants walked beside us, two on either side, carrying a large canopy to shade us from the sun.

"Has it ever struck you," said Mother, "how some fruits stay inside your mouth, while others disintegrate the moment they touch your tongue?"

She'd stopped suddenly, and the canopy-servants had carried on like sleepwalkers, oblivious to the world. They mumbled to each other and walked backwards slowly, counting, until the canopy was over our heads again.

"Watermelons, for instance," said Mother, holding the word on her tongue carefully, as if it was an explanation in itself. "Delicious, but not what I'd call a *useful* fruit. As soon as the ruby flesh is in the mouth . . . puf!" She flung her fingers wide like stars. "One sweet swallow and it's gone."

We carried on walking. I chased her chain of thought around my head. She was being very nice to me and I liked it. I didn't want her to suddenly change and I knew that she would snap at me, if she thought I was too stupid to understand what she meant.

"Whereas *oranges*," she went on grandly, "*grapefruits*, soft pears and over-ripened *plums* . . ." She could almost have been boastfully listing the royal families who'd attended my wedding, ". . . these are *useful* fruits."

We stopped again and mother looked at me. I didn't smile, so that she'd know that I was trying very hard.

"These are fruits to hold inside your mouth, in small, thoughtfully arranged pieces," she went on. "Then, just at that moment when the pressure is applied, just at that moment when your mouth is shaped like an omicron, at the same time as you're slipping downwards, as smoothly and slowly as dripping honey, the fruits release their juices, and make the sliding, the sucking, the kissing and the *swallowing* so much . . . *sweeter.*"

I could hear the tap-tap-tapping of garden-slaves driving bamboo sticks into the soil, somewhere past the avocados. I thought that no matter how hard I tried I could never apply charcoal around my eyes so precisely as my mother, and that my hair would never shine so brilliantly, and that my back would never be as straight.

She linked our arms more tightly and patted my hand. Under the canopy it was just the two of us, and she hadn't snapped at me, or called me stupid. We carried on walking. She had nowhere to rush off to, nowhere more important to be, and she stayed with me for the rest of the day, answering all my questions and telling me more of her secrets.

3. *A Later Episode*

On a day when the sky colours like bruised fruit, our floating cortège brushes the spongy sides of the west bank of the Nile. We are blown along by Zeus' breath, and He cries rain on the shrouded body as it is conveyed, meanderingly, through the fearsome shadows of the necropolis.

It seems inevitable that Laius has met a violent end, since he always carried violence in him. Not all the stories were true, of course, although it could be that I stopped listening, after I'd run from the palace, barefoot, my inner thighs stained raspberry red. It was my brother, Creon, who took me back, even though I begged him in our parents' house and clung on to him as I had done as a child. But my childhood faded to a foggy memory, when I was handed over from my brother to the King.

"Remember the oracle's warning," Creon said. "Long live King Laius!" Laius held me as I shook. "You have helped save the life of a King," he said. "Never forget it. The life of a King."

They made me their accomplice.

The physician measured out a herbal sleeping draught and dripped it on my extended tongue, as if I was a fledgling. Its bitterness seemed fitting. During the night, Laius stayed close as the sleeping draught drowned me. In the moments I surfaced, choking for breath, I felt him gripping my hand, as if he was pulling me towards the shore. Once, he carried me out on the balcony and I sucked in air that smelled of eucalyptus. Clouds, like creamy ribbons, rippled across the moon, and I listened to the lonely happiness of hyenas. In my dream they licked their lips around my bleeding groin. The pain was immense, as if they were gnawing at my bones. My husband's eyes shone yellow in the shadowy room, and his stinking breath was panting as I struggled, half in, half out of consciousness.

The burial procession twists, snake-like, around the giant tombs. Death songs whine in the wind and our funeral garments stream out behind us like banners.

In the morning, the hyenas were gone, the trees were as still as statues and Laius slumped across the foot of my bed as if he was set in stone. I searched his sleeping face for signs of cruelness but only saw an old man, his skin in creases, his hair sticking up in snowy tufts.

I didn't really know him. He was spoiled for choice with serving girls and houseboys, all so much more experienced and skilful than I was. And he never asked me questions or talked to me, like I'd heard him talking to his friends. He woke up as if my thoughts had whispered to him in his dreams. He said, "Tell me what I can give you," and I said, "Give me one story about when you were a little boy."

The burial lasts two, immeasurable days. Time passes in a confusion of weeping, falling bodies, and relentless wailing. Creon tears out a piece of his hair. He tells me to be on my guard, for unseen enemies. On the third day, twenty bullocks pull us back, slowly, against a downward wind, their tongues lolling from side to side with the mighty effort. Mourners line the river banks, throwing circles of laurel and peach blossom into the water.

At dusk we arrive back at the palace. The sky hangs low like a damson about to split its skin.

Creon says, "Come with me and my family. You'll be safer." But I insist that I stay in my chambers, behind bolted doors, with the Palace Guards on duty through the night.

"It's what I want," I say, and my voice sounds alien to everyone's ears, even my own.

That night, sparks fly from Zeus' whip as He lashes the country with a storm. Jewels set in the palace walls glitter with every flash of light. I hear armour rattling, and pounding footsteps, as soldiers run past my window, seeking shelter. There are no arms held out for me. For the first time in my life, I am alone with my own fear. And it makes me understand the power of men.

"Be calm, be calm," I say, aloud, and my widow's voice belongs to nobody but me.

"I was the kind of boy," Laius said, "who cried for his mother, who hid his face in his nurse's skirts, who ran away when he heard his father's footsteps. I followed the washing women down to the river and learned all their songs and all their dances. My pet kid was called Two-Shakes because he shook his head two times, like this, whenever anyone walked near him.

My father was growing angrier and angrier. Whenever he caught my mother kissing me, or serving girls putting ribbons in my hair, he bellowed, 'This won't teach him how to be a King!'

One morning, before it was light, before anyone in the household was awake, he took me from my bed, in my sleeping-shirt, my eyes still glued together, and he carried me and Two-Shakes up the side of a mountain. He asked me what I did with my mother and I told him I showed her the dances I knew and sang her some songs. So he said, 'Sing them for me now,' and I sang one. Then he said, 'Sing another one,' and as I started singing, he started walking towards Two-Shakes and Two-Shakes shook his head twice, like this, and started walking backwards on the mountain. Still I carried on singing, laughing at Two-Shakes, and Two-Shakes still shook his head. Then my father snatched something quickly from Two-Shakes' neck, and Two-Shakes screamed and there was a flash and a sparkle and a bright streak of red at Two-Shakes' neck. And then he shook his head, just once, like this, and crumpled to the ground like a pile of washing.

My father held the knife up to my face and made me lick the blood. I could only taste the salt, splashing from my eyes. And then he put the knife against my throat and said, 'Never, ever, sing those songs again,' and he took me down the mountain and he taught me how to be a King."

4. *The Final Episode*

Isn't it lovely, the beat of the rain? He used to say to me, "Sshh, listen to the rain." I'd never thought to stop and open up my ears before. Strange, isn't it, that you can spend your whole life thinking that you're comfortable and contented, and then, one rain-soaked afternoon, lying beneath your lover's body, he puts his lips against your ear . . . "Sshh," and you hear things you've never heard before. Nothing else matters then, only that one moment, the weight of him on you, the touch of his lips, rain, drumming . . .

We put up with all the predictable comments. Mutton. Lamb. Cradle-snatching. Fortune-chasing. It was amusing at first, then tedious, then people stopped altogether. They saw how we were with each other.

I was self-conscious to begin with — and *nervous*! The first time . . . he had to ply me with drink. He told me he'd been longing and waiting and praying . . . I thought it was a fad, fashionable, the 'older woman' syndrome. But he said he was *lusting* for me. He made me laugh! He could make me laugh . . .

I tried to kill the candles — the *embarrassment*! — but he insisted. It was me he wanted, he said, all of me, as I was, as I am. Miserable, I felt. I hid my face . . . I tried to hide my belly . . . and my breasts! As he unwound each layer of clothing, I seemed to flop, crumble . . . my camouflage was peeled away and I was left as bare as trussed-up meat, waiting for the hot breath of a flaming oven. I burned with shame. I wept.

"Go back to your golden nymphets," I told him. "Go back and revel in their firmness, their softness, their perfect unused bodies!"

"I'm used," I told him. "Used goods. Leave me to eat figs and grow fat!"

I cried, lying there, desperate for a sheet, a cloth — any scrap to hide me. But he wrapped his arms around me and showed me his erection.

"Is *this* proof enough for you?" he said. "I'm *mad* for you. What more do I have to do?"

We laughed and cried and talked that first night. His fingers travelled slowly across the great maps etched upon my belly. "Beautiful," he told me. "What a mesmerising journey that would be."

But he was patient. Not until I believed in us, he said, then the time would be right.

"We have the rest of our lives together," he said. "What's between us shouldn't be hurried."

It was as if we'd known each other all our lives. All our lives. It was.

He made me come with his tongue. I went to places I'd never imagined . . . exquisiteness . . . Now I can only imagine his head, returning to where it had already been. . .

They pulled him screaming from between my legs. I heard his cries, his desperate cries for life, as if he knew what we had in store for him . . . If only I'd had the courage to place my hand across his tiny face! To smother his baby nose and mouth, to take away his innocent, sweet-scented breath. I could have saved him from the sharpened spike that would pierce his chubby feet; the lonely winds of a deserted hilltop; wolves circling, their mouths dripping, moving nearer . . . what kind of a mother am I!

I wished I could keep him deep inside, revolving in my fluid for ever. I knew that the life he had lived inside me was the happiest he would ever know. I knew it then. The oracle had spoken. I turned my face to the wall as they dragged him out of me, carried him away. It had to be.

They didn't know the pain, the aching, the longing I was left with, the unfillable spaces . . . unfillable until I met Oedipus . . . until he was given back to me. God's cruel joke. My punishment. My wicked, heartless-mother punishment. But I loved him. I loved him as he was scraped and pulled and torn away, as I felt his tiny, bloody limbs leaving me forever, and I loved him when he came back to me, when he kissed and caressed and fondled the spaces that were once his home. He must have longed to climb back inside! To swim and turn and sleep inside me.

And now . . . it's raining more heavily. As if it will never stop.

"Sshh. Close your eyes and imagine it's raining diamonds," he told me. "Marry me and every shower that falls on you will be filled with jewels."

"Jewels would hurt me though," I said to him, looking at the lights inside his eyes.

"Then I could kiss you better. Kiss all your sparkling wounds."

Perhaps he'll see me sometimes, in his dreams. Perhaps he'll walk outside on days like this, turn his face upwards, feel the pain of diamonds on his skin. Perhaps that's when he'll think of me.

Rose Meets a Man

HELEN CROSS

Helen Cross *is 29 years old. She lives in Norwich where she is working on a novel.*

Rose Springer knocked on her boss's door, peeped her head round and seeing Ed Mutter cosy in his executive winter wear, she smiled and said:

"You can have me now, Ed, or you can have me later."

"Now there's an offer I couldn't refuse," Ed said, bouncing back in his padded orthopaedic chair. There was a beery whiff in the air. On many occasions Rose had heard Ed blame the pressures of local government for the withering of his radical student politics and the strengthening of his student drinking habits.

"Though it's a bit early in the morning for me, Rose," he said. The grin which was growing on his face heaped his skin in curving drifts around his mouth: his bushy black eyebrows spiked upwards as though caught in a sudden gust of wind. Rose noticed a crescent of thermal vest winking between each button of his checked, woollen shirt, as he rocked in his chair.

"I'll come back," Rose said. She heard the hot-air heater growling ferociously in the corner of the room and saw a wide blush of condensation dappling the window. Why'd she not simply said, *You can see me now Ed, or you can see me later?* Outside the door she closed her eyes and heard the words as though she were still speaking them. She felt the sick flush of embarrassment. She had just come on to Ed Mutter. How do such things happen? It felt as though the office were tilting.

At home that evening Rose dropped her bag at the door and went upstairs and tussled her tight, bright Christmas clothes onto the bedroom floor and stood naked, looking at the body in the mirror and the snow falling over the fields behind. It was eighteen months since any other human body had seen the supple dip of her waist, the way her curly black hair rested on her naked shoulders and slung down over her back. *Oui, je suis thurty tree but I owe it to my bootifool breests to be viv a maaaaan zoon,* she said in the foreign accent she'd used privately at night since she was seven. Then she turned round; the front was the nice bit, what was not so nice was the way her upper thighs displayed a pale, mottled hue like slabs of stale corned beef. Rose's mother had the same spongy, bovine thighs. Before too long I'll have Mrs Springer's speckled, ham-ish upper arms too, Rose thought.

Rose sat on the bed and looked at clothes bursting out of drawers and disappearing down the side of the chest of drawers. She looked at her grubby dressing-table on which was piled assorted ancient junk; a ten-year-old pot of blue nail varnish, several broken bricks of sparkling eye-shadow, gummed up eyebrow tweezers, unusable, modish hair curlers, a crushed box of Regular Tampax, a black lipstick nestling at the bottom of a tattered straw bowl, a dusty purple G-string with a top-hat sequinned to the front (this was wrapped around a deodorant canister), and a plastic folder containing a working brief of the Rio Earth Summit 1992. She moved to an armchair, humped over with jackets and cardigans, and with the cool eye she clinically cast over corporate problems she thought again of Ed Mutter and began to assess whether she was wearing garments intended for a much younger, more radical woman.

When Rose first rented her own place, after the split from Bruce, her lover of two years, she'd tidy the house, clearing away the dirty washing, sweeping the litter off the dressing-table into the top drawer and then making and smoothing the bed before she went out, in case she met anyone. That way, on impulse, she could decide to bring them home for the night. Whilst getting ready she'd put on records and dance around the house, saying *Oui, Ja, Yees, anyting cooed appen tonight.* But it didn't happen and now she was coming on to Ed Mutter. She thought of confusing conversations in smoky pubs; flirtatious, fickle exchanges at bright barbecues; wearying debates with the smart boyfriends of her smitten girlfriends. Each time by midnight her instinct was familiar; I *wouldn't even walk round the corner with any of these men.*

When Rose did meet a keen, unusual man, as she had in a street in West London on a hot summer night (a lean black man riding a bike had screeched to a halt beside her and said, *"Hey lovely, you going home alone? — now, you come home with me tonight, you're beautiful, come home with me, I like you, I want you, I can make you happy, give you a hot time"*) the situation instantly became too wonderful, too immediately precious to risk it all by impulsive action. She didn't feel easy about giving in, letting it happen. She got frightened, didn't say a word and he cycled off. A part of her still felt like the least agile animal in the jungle and the skills of sexual resistance she'd honed as a teenager still clung to her like Lycra. But you are grown up and capable and old enough to take the initiative, she told herself, but should it be presented as a question: Do You Want To Come Home With Me Tonight? or as a statement: I Want To Spend The Night With You!

I'm too old to be fooled, she thought later that night, and the consequence of this is I'm being denied the chance to be foolish. But Ed Mutter. She still felt woozy.

On Tuesday morning she had an important meeting with the Marketing Department. She liked Don Wiley, the Head of Press, Publicity and Public Relations, because he never made her uneasy by referring to anything personal. This morning Rose walked into his office and saw him suddenly smile. He put a hand to his mouth and turned back to his papers. Don had three teenage children and a caravan in Devon. He was serious and industrious, with a methodical heaviness which some people at Reddock Council called charmless. Rose looked down at her navy suit and saw that the top button of her blouse had come undone and the black-lace bra, which had a white pearl stitched between the cups, was fully exposed. She was showing everything. She stood there for a moment, then they looked at one another, but not like colleagues, and Don wrinkled his nose in an unfamiliar, jocular way. Then with a lilt of a laugh in his voice he swivelled away from her on his chair and said, "When you are ready Rosa, toot sweet."

In this meeting it became clear Rose had made a big mistake. The Environmental Resources Department, of which she was Head, had initiated a scheme whereby as from today local people could bring along their Christmas trees and have them pulped into environmentally friendly garden compost for free. Since 9 a.m. people had been arriving in the car park glumly carrying their snow-sprinkled trees and the pulper had not been booked until the following week. Rose could not imagine how she had made such a big mistake. She was methodically organized; she would check and double-check and then get someone else to check for her. Fear, she'd hitherto assumed, made her faultless.

That night was so cold Rose put on a jumper over her pyjamas and a pair of walking socks before she got into bed. She had a dream. She was getting on a train in a crazy assemblage of clothes: a pair of stockings, a tiny leather miniskirt, a thick fisherman's jumper, black stiletto heels, sunglasses and a flat cap with a peacock feather at the peak. She was waving to her wizened parents who stood far off in the distance on an ancient, rural platform abandoned in drifts of snow. Her mother, politely crease-proof in polite Marks and Spencer's separates, was watching Rose with puzzled concern. Her father was angrily shaking his fat head and weeping. Bruce stood shocked but firm behind this frail, desperate, grey couple, resting one hand on her mother's shoulder. The train chugged and screeched but didn't quite manage to pull away and Bruce kept calling out, *Goodbye, Keep Warm!*

By 10 a.m. on Wednesday morning the office furniture was nudging Rose when she walked past, and when she put things down surfaces slyly retracted an inch or so, showering her with coffee, staples, pens, and paper clips. She sat at her desk and tried not to move about too much for fear of attracting disasters.

The presence in the corner of the room of Thom Fry, a recent graduate, rippled the stillness. Thom was Rose's most precocious member of staff. He was 22 and irked almost everyone in the building with his university jokes and his enthusiasm for his new job. A few of the girls who were not irritated by him found him exotic and unashamed. He was probably the first Cambridge graduate Reddock Council had ever recruited, and if Rose exerted any pull in Personnel he would be the last. While she sat looking from blank screen to loaded winter whiteness, Thom was resting his cheek on his fist and watching her from his desk at the windowless side of the office. At polytechnic Rose had developed a couple of adoring passions for bold, blonde public schoolboys; she'd wanted to be hitched to their confidence. It was a sign of how far she'd come that Thom was just like all other men she met: an hilariously unattractive proposition. Still, today Rose could hear Thom's thoughts bubbling away behind her and was suddenly inspired with the certainty that he was wondering about her limitations as a boss; trying to assess what foxy tricks she'd employed to secure her steady and unexpected promotion within the department. It didn't feel to Rose like paranoia, it felt like a premonition. He's wondering about the potency of my powers, Rose thought, not turning or moving. He won't be able to instantly put his finger on what exactly pisses him off about me, she thought, but he will sit there scheming in his embroidered waistcoat and fucking fluorescent shirt until he finds a theory that fits.

Thom strolled over and stood behind her chair.

"Hey, Rosie, cheer up. What's got seventy-five balls and screws old ladies?"

"Thom, I'm confident I'm not the person you think I am."

"Bingo."

"Who do you think you are?"

She thought she'd spoken evenly and calmly, presenting the sentence as a philosophical inquiry rather than an insult, but when she'd finished, the office went very quiet and everyone turned and looked at Rose. It was not a simple misunderstanding because as she'd spoken Rose felt a sudden, word-impeding, squirt in her mouth, and the hot injection of liquid tasted metallic and vile.

"Hey, it's just a joke."

That night Rose piled on cardigans to keep warm and drank a bottle of red wine to swill the bile from her mouth. Blushed by the firelight she listened to scratched vinyl pop records, and, with a fierce incredulity which the wine didn't dull, she ran over the earlier scene again and again. *Who the hell do I think I am?* The shrill tone — for now she realised how she'd spoken to Thom, loud and angry and shrill — was one she only ever used with Bruce. She felt guilty about Bruce. He was a good, unusual, kind and unconventional man; he worked as Deputy Head in a primary school, he made his own Christmas cards, he read books and cooked casseroles, he'd walked the Pennine Way — she was the only person she knew who found him boring. She felt guilty about Thom; he was a bright, funny kid, everyone else got the jokes. She felt guilty about her mother; the way, maybe, perhaps, she used her powerful job to imply superiority. She felt weary feeling guilty. *Ach, je ne sais pas vot's zappening do me!*

Rose went to bed drunk, mumbling the joke she would make tomorrow morning when she humbly, calmly and responsibly apologised to Thom.

On Thursday at 2 p.m., Derek Best, Reddock Council's Executive Director said, "Pine needles," during an emergency meeting of the Senior Management Team, which had been called to discuss the pulper emergency. Rose sniffed and caught the drift of moist vegetation, of minty freshness, of clean mountain air. She smelt it so strongly that she got up from her chair without thinking and raised her chin at the window and took several deep breaths. Rose guessed by the way Derek Best looked at her out of one sly eye that he'd seen such impulsiveness in women many times before, but was astonished to glimpse it in the Head of Environmental Resources. Derek Best was a competition cyclist, and beneath his fine linen suit he proudly exhibited the rippling physique of a prize ox. He dropped his pen on the desk, put his hands behind his head and sighed at the four other suited members of the Senior Management Team.

"Let's not get the problem out of proportion," said Don Wiley. He wrinkled his nose sympathetically in Rose's direction and his sweet smile succeeded in immediately returning her mind to Tuesday's incident.

Elsewhere in the room, Ed Mutter doodled interlocking cubes over his agenda, and young Rod Singleton, the Management Services Coordinator who was known to panic and explode at inappropriate moments, said, "Hell Derek, we must address the problem immediately. We damn well have to put a damage limitation policy into operation, right now. The heat is well and truly on." And with these words Rose smelt burning, a burning so pungent she was forced, though she knew it to be rash and stupid, to jump up from her chair and stand in the centre of the room.

The odour was that of a fiercely hot iron singeing foam; a sour, crackling smell. Derek Best coughed and slammed around a pile of papers, then took a very long drink of water. She stood there in the middle of the room and stared straight out of the window at the bare branches of the horse chestnut tree. I don't meet men, she thought, because I am in an inappropriate environment. They were all looking at her. The room was silent but for Rod Singleton's quick, heavy breathing and the scratching of Ed's ball point. In meetings Rose avoided this sort of awkward situation by using a number of techniques to smoothly circumnavigate the difference in sex, age and attitude between her and her senior management colleagues. She imagined she looked like Mrs Springer taking shorthand, circa 1959. She'd give her body a slow, leaden languor and never do things too quickly, she'd smile sometimes rather than speak, she'd cross her legs and make her spine very straight.

The smell was getting fiercer. Everyone said, no, they could not, when she finally asked if they could smell anything.

The Senior Management Team resolved they would set up a Christmas Tree crèche in one corner of the car park where owners could tie their names to their trees and leave them until the pulper finally arrived.

At home that evening everything was back to normal. The house smelt like a damp flannel as it usually did in winter. She puddled around, putting on records and dancing to them in the kitchen and smoking far too many cigarettes and calling her friends. It was all absolutely normal but when she tried to settle down to re-read an important section of the Rio Earth Report she realised she still felt looser, not in the moral sense but in the sense sense.

She wrestled in her sleep, feeling one minute hotly oppressed by the heavy duvet, the next desperate for its cool close touch. She got up and from the window watched slices of snow shifting on neighbouring tiles. The moon was only a sliver away from being full. Last year when a full moon coincided with the start of her period, she'd calmly started an important dismissal procedure in a stern, unquestionable manner and ended with a trembling lip. But this was not the same, it wouldn't wane. She wasn't quite shipwrecked she told herself, as she slipped into sleep, *but zoon.*

All week Pete Freeman had been working around Rose's building on a special publicity project; photographing all the council buildings and services for new promotional pictures. For the last three days he'd been trying to get in touch with her; to make contact, to show his portfolio, but each time he'd called from reception she'd fobbed him off; too busy, perhaps later, after the meeting. By late afternoon on Friday, even though it was nearly dark and more snow was starting to fall, he was still hanging around; she was, he insisted, the only manager he had not been able to see. It's Friday, she thought, I could ruin your weekend. He continued, saying that he wouldn't be over this way for quite some time, and it seemed a shame to waste the opportunity, and anyway, he said cheekily, I fancy a drink. She relaxed and said did he realise the situation she was in? — the scene in the car park was reminiscent of a pagan ceremony; stern-faced, snow-splattered men and women clutching pine trees in an empty, blizzard stormed car park. He said he understood. She said she'd meet him in the pub across the road for a quick drink.

"Get me a bottle of Pils," she said, before he'd even offered to buy her a drink.

"I'll line them up."

"You got any cigarettes?"

"I'll get you some."

She stamped her feet and snow fell off in thick wedges on the crimson carpet in the bar. The roads were getting treacherous and she might even get snowed in for the weekend. She strode over to where he was sitting at the side of the bar. She sat down and started to fall in love.

She felt it coming on in the way that earlier in the month she had sensed the start of bad flu; with a small uneasiness somewhere in the body. Outside, orange puffs of snow were curling under the street lamps. The first serious tickle was the way she watched his hands as he talked about his job, then the way she could clearly see every shadow when he described his basement flat, the expectant feeling she had in her stomach when he mentioned his small niece (it turned out his sister was separated from her husband, so Pete had offered to have the kid two evenings a week). The symptoms were all over her body, she was too weak to resist, even her fingertips pulsed with a sick longing to touch the purple scar he had across one cheek.

If she could just get home she'd need to see no one for the next two days, she'd lie in bed with Lemsip and a hot-water bottle and recover. The full moon would pass, the pulper would arrive, the Senior Management Team would forget, and Thom would live to crack another joke. In time, the image of her black-lace bra would fade in Don Wiley's mind.

"I've booked in for the night at the hotel opposite the station. Because of the weather. I drive an ancient ex-Red Cross Ambulance Van when I've got all my equipment with me and I wouldn't want to risk the drive in this weather. It's getting deep."

"Right. You wouldn't want to risk it. You'll drive back tomorrow?"

"First thing. I'm photographing a church steeple in the afternoon."

"I think I need a doctor."

"Sorry?"

"Nothing, sorry. Right, well. You're right, you mustn't get stuck in the snow."

"I think it'll be dangerous out here tonight. I hope you're not driving anywhere. D'you live in Reddock?"

"A short drive."

"Be careful," he said, and paused to smile at her. Rose felt her limbs aching, her joints pulsing. "Another drink?"

"I must go. The snow."

"You sure?"

"The snow," and she raised her hot, heavy arms in a gesture of hopelessness.

"What will you do tonight, Rose?" Pete said, unzipping his leather jacket and settling down into the red velvet chair.

"Housework." She took a small breath; she'd spoken without thinking and could've picked on any equally wild activity: gymnastics, gardening, sun-bathing. Rose's stomach had that tingling chill which means the flu is going to be very serious.

"Housework?"

"Hmm, perhaps."

"You don't really strike me as the kind of woman to go home at 8 p.m. after several bottles of Pils and half a packet of Silk Cut and do *housework*."

"And just what are you implying, Mr Freeman?" she said, straightening her back and tucking in her chin in a burlesque of proud annoyance. He laughed.

"How about we go and have something to eat? I'm starving. Your canteen was very disturbing."

"Oh, I've got to go, no. The snow."

"I can't persuade you?"

"I can't."

"A quick pizza?"

"It's too dangerous," she said, and felt the sentence distorting in her inner ear and knew that the next day the love would've paralysed her whole head.

"Well, before you do I'd like to quickly show you my portfolio, you know just in case anything comes up in the future you could use me for?"

"Yes, but I must go soon, I don't really feel very well and it's Friday and it's been a rather terrible week if I'm honest with you. But yes, I'd like to see it.' Rose feared the illness was making her a little hysterical. Her birth sign was Cancer; they make poor patients.

Pete took Rose through a sequence of architectural pictures of European buildings. He explained the needs of each client and the budget for each commission. Rose watched the way the veins in his forearm pushed against the pale surface of his skin when he turned the pages. She forced her sore eyes to focus on the pictures. Can't he see I'm poorly? she thought. On one side of the album was pasted a technicolor blow-up of an office window, triangular green bricks spiked round a frame of shining blue steel, a slash of sunlight across the surrounding red brick.

"This is in Cologne," he said, and turned the page to reveal an arrangement of smaller photographs of city roundabouts and street signs.

"Peterborough," he said, and looked at her so firmly that Rose was sure he was going to refer to her illness.

"Well, thanks for showing these to me,' she said when he closed

the book. "You've done a great job, and if anything suitable comes up in the future, I'll remember. You've made it all look wonderful."
"Well, it's a wonderful life," Pete said, and turned to look out of the window. "Particularly so, I think, when it's snowing."

"Pete, I've really got to go," Rose said, and Pete stood up to shake her hand. The touch was tonic to her; his skin cool and soft as butter. It reminded Rose of how, when she'd puked as a child, Mrs Springer would cup Rose's forehead in a wide, firm palm and Rose would yield like wax, relaxing all her feeble weight, trusting in her mother's refreshing, safe embrace.

Rose's house was exactly 8.3 miles from the council buildings. Tonight the lonely road she drove along was sugared with a frail lace of ice, the thick snowflakes instantly becoming skeletal when they hit the grit. The moon was on her left, fat and full, but obscured behind a gauze of snow cloud. Her headlights made the road a yellow cone of light. Pete had walked her to the car and then gone off to check into his hotel, walking backwards in the darkness, waving into the night. At the furthest edge of where the headlights reached, she saw something small scuttle into the road. A few months earlier, thundering along this road to work, Rose had killed a pheasant and, when she'd looked in her rear view mirror, had seen a red-and-brown cloud of swirling feathers.

Rose was sensible, not sentimental, about wildlife. If she'd had a normal week, if she hadn't said, smelt, felt and seen such things she would've probably just kept going and hoped that the poor thing would move and if it didn't, or if it hesitated, panicked and dived into the centre of the road, she'd hit it — it was the safest thing to do. But the last five days had made her uncertain as to the control she exerted over her own body. Tonight she couldn't kill a living thing.

She wasn't driving very fast and she touched the break gently with her still-trembling, love-stricken leg. The back wheels of the car shimmied sexily on the ice. She pressed the brake more firmly, and responding instantly to her touch, the front wheels started to glide. The car was not slowing but floating in a fearless, impulsive, careless way. She felt her left arm go rigid as though cement were hardening in her veins. Then her right arm did the same — her elbow wedged against the door, fixing her hand in a fierce grip against the wheel. One jellied foot was pumping on the brake, with all the stricken strength she possessed, the other was jammed to the floor. In this way she became pressed, tall and flat, like a racing driver in the seat.

The moon was no longer on her left, but right in front of her. The snow had stopped, the cloud was clearing. The car was travelling sideways. She saw fields and farmhouses and dark shadows of machinery she had never looked at before. A house high up on the side of the hill, a glinting barn, a truck-load of scaffolding. Every second, sight and sound was like a note in a slow song. She was a single string, plucked. She pictured her mother as she looked when they used to walk in the wood together in the spring: bronze flecks of sunlight on her hazel hair and the sound of a woodpigeon cooing. Rose lifted her foot, the car still sliding, and she unlocked her arm and afterwards she wondered if she had closed her eyes. Relaxed and floating she felt young and weightless — *Kay sera sera* — *zis is zit.* For a second she was just there in the car in the luminous night and she didn't feel afflicted anymore.

Then a loud rumble of wheels against the verge, the churning of frozen turf, the staggering, rattling, trembling halt of the car.

Rose was on the opposite side of the road. The car, its back wheels balanced on the icy bank, was snorting and facing the town. She didn't recognize what stretched before her as the road down which she had travelled every morning for the last eighteen months, or even as the road down which she had, only a few minutes earlier, driven with feverish tears scalding her flaming cheeks. She felt cold, but not poorly, alert but not crazy, thirty-three but sixteen, smart but dirty, responsible but untamed, filial but duty-free.

To congratulate herself Rose tried to shake her own hand, and the recognition that this was a bipedal impossibility made her giggle uncontrollably. She lit a cigarette and wondered how to celebrate. *Mon cherie, zoo are alive in zee bootifool verld* — *zelebrate.* And the jubilee must involve, Rose thought when she had stopped laughing, some talking, some listening, some touching, and some kissing.

Extract from
A Gift of Stones

ANNA GARRY

__Anna Garry__ lives in Norwich. She is currently working on a novel, A Gift of Stones.

Writer's note: Theresa, the main character, has recently moved from Ireland to England.

England, 1967

"Fiona Jackson's farted. Fiona Jackson's farted."

"I didn't."

"You did."

"I did not."

Fiona's skinny legs swing back and forth under her desk, like the legs of a daddy-long-legs. And you can never get comfortable on these hard, slippery chairs.

"Give me a clothes peg!" That's Christine with the white, white socks.

"You stink."

"I don't."

"You do."

Stop. Why don't they stop? Fiona's smelly, her hair's full of knots, and sometimes her hands look like they've been dipped in dirty water. But you have to feel sorry for her. She has only one dress. And two dresses make all the difference.

Fart is a dirty word. Like pigs snuffling in a trough. Snort. Snort. Snort. Fart. Fart. Fart. They have to stop now. The smell's gone, hasn't it? And Nip the dog runs happily across the reading book. He sees Jane.

Let the smell go away. Please. Red-hot cheeks, someone will see. Fiona's always called names, so she's used to it. Fiona farts, that's what she does. Won't do it again. Promise. And God's forgiving, so he is.

God knows about the first day at this school. Standing in front of all those eyes, staring, staring so hard that if you looked down there was sure to be huge eyes all over the new dress. Being gawped at is the worst. Anything, just anything to stop it happening again.

And being seven years old, and clever. Well that's gone out the window. Sometimes it's hard to hear what the other girls are saying. The words come at you through cotton wool. Like being at the sea-side and slipping under the water. If you wiggle your fingers in each ear and shake your head, the water comes out. But that doesn't work now; the only thing left is to watch mouths. Gaping, scrinching, pulling mouths.

And there's that postbox. Write about a postman, says Miss Best, then draw a big postbox and a letter to put inside. Drawing's great, better than writing. Miss Best doesn't like joined writing, it's wrong. Write like me, she says, each letter with a space in between.

Tongue out, careful not to bite it. A tall straight pillar. A black pencil for the bottom, colour carefully, and then Christine's deep-green pencil. Bending closer makes sure there isn't a bit of white left. Now for Miss Best.

"Theresa dear, a postbox is red. Like this." And she points to Jane Egan's shiny pencil case. "Now it's a lovely postbox. You just rub out the green, and colour it red. You do have a red pencil?"

Yes, Miss Best. No, Miss Best. Three bags full, Miss Best. But she's a right eijit. Postboxes are green. She can't want a red one. But good girls don't answer back and Mammy wants a good girl. So back to the desk, rubbing green curls to blow on the floor. And what do we have? A rotten purple postbox, a wrinkled copybook, and all because Miss Best wants red.

But what happens after that? Sitting in the van, by a traffic-lights. There it is, a postbox. A tall, brilliant-red postbox. Does Gerard know? Or Tim? Prickles all over and sweaty arms. Postboxes are red, and Miss Best is right. And Theresa Lenehan is a thicko and a stupid little girl.

Creeping out of bed at night you can lean on the window ledge and look out. Straight ahead are houses, and above, a strip of orange sky, like being inside an old biscuit tin with the lid a little bit open. If only you could reach up and push the lid right off, then there would be a wide black sky and stars.

These houses are something. All stuck together with a gap now and then for roads. There might be tiny chinks between each one, at least enough to let the air through. Then some day those gaps will widen, the houses shake and stand free, like trees.

And the whole area is red. Not a happy red, but a blackish red that goes shiny in the rain. Rows and rows of red houses force you left, then right and down the hill to school. The iron gates stretch wide, like rotten teeth, and gobble all the girls round about.

Little girls shouldn't look out of windows. That's what Daddy says. But he doesn't know. No one knows, except that rude man who waved last week, his fingers pushed up like barbed wire. Nasty man. A horrible man like that doesn't have children.

Number nine is straight ahead. Left is number seven and right is number eleven. The dark makes doors look black and shivery, like wide barn doors at home. In the day there's an orange door, a green door and two white doors. Number nine's a pretty house with a plant pot on the steps. A lady pours tea leaves on her flower. God says you should love your neighbour, so every Sunday at mass God is asked for another flower. That would make her smile. Maybe.

The windows at night are like bright stamps on a dark envelope. They disappear and then blink back on, always when you aren't looking, no matter how hard you stare and stare. At number fifteen things happen all the time. Lights on one minute and off the next, like the whole family are running up and down the stairs flicking the light switches. On off, off off on. They must be rich, or maybe they're playing hide-and-seek.

Number five is different. There's a lady and man shouting. Then slam goes the front door, scream goes the lady, and stomp goes the man down the steps. It's not nice to look. And crouching down you get wet, a damp strip down your pyjamas' arm. Daddy says it's the steam on the windows. One last look and back to bed.

There's a knack to washing knickers, that's what Granny says. But

Granny has a scrubbing-board, a huge bar of white soap, and she has a wringer. Oh that wringer. The soggy covers are tamed. The towels stiffened. Nothing gets the better of the wringer. You hold the heavy clothes to its mouth, Granny turns the handle, and they are swallowed slowly and come out so light that you can easily carry them to the line. If only Granny was here now.

The knickers have to be washed, and the boys' underpants. And the blue dress with the milk stain down the front. The bucket is full, the water as cold as putting your hand in a rain barrel, and the green soap so hard that the best thing is to jump on it. But it might get you back and send you slipping across the room to land legs-out on your bottom.

It has to be done. The blue dress smells sour, like old vomit. No way is anyone at school going to point and say, "You stink." But what if the dress looks worse after washing? What if it looks like Fiona Jackson's arms, with great washes of lines where the dirt has got stuck, or where the soap doesn't work?

In and out quickly, that's the trick. Then your fingers don't feel like ice. They hurt, but you can move them. And if you rub really hard the soap gets a little slippy. Next time ask Daddy to boil some water. But he's out looking for work, pacing the streets he calls it. And when he gets home he looks like someone's poured water over him and darkened his eyes. Tired, pet, he'll say, mighty tired.

The two knickers make a wet pile by the bucket. A dunk of the last pair, then a hard scrub until the knuckles prickle and fingers freeze. Done. Rinse now, Granny says. So off to the sink and the water runs over them, like stones in the stream. Squeezing out is as bad as washing. No matter how hard you twist, the things still drip. Well they're done. That's it. No one can say that Theresa Lenehan has smelly knickers.

Up the steps, past sleeping Mammy, to the boys' room. The attic is big enough for a mattress and a washing-line which stretches from a nail in one corner to the window. A peg for each knickers and they're hung. The baggy grey knickers drip like the branches of trees in a summer storm. Soon they'll be dry and ready to wear.

Bang, crunch, creak. Each step makes a different noise when you jump.

"For God's sake, Theresa, what are you doing?"

"Nothing, Mammy."

Then the steps become as soft as snow, and you tiptoe so there isn't a sound to be heard. Now for the rest.

Bread, bread, potatoes, and more bread. That's all there is to eat. Where have carrots gone? And gravy? And the stews with bits of meat floating in them? And Mammy's stopped cooking. She just shuffles around from the teapot to the chair by the fire. She's like a half-blown balloon, swollen out front, and flat behind. If someone blew her hard enough she'd become round all over, like a turnip or a cabbage.

And what about Dolly? She's sitting on top of the box in Granny's shed. She has to be cold; that shed's full of drafts. And next to her are the beds, the chairs, the kitchen table, and the big wardrobe. All our things. Mammy wouldn't let Dolly go inside with Granny. She said Granny has enough clutter without Dolly.

Daddy hasn't a job. That's the problem. What are we doing in this strange town, in this strange country, says Mammy. You were supposed to be working, says Mammy. I can't help it if the job fell through, says Daddy. We have to wait, says Daddy. When there's enough money we'll bring across the furniture, says Daddy. Then there's shouting and crying, enough to drive you under the blankets, even if it's daytime.

Daddy never mentions Dolly, or Tim's teddy bear. But you know not to ask him. You know it's best to be quiet. Gerard asked why we were here when everything was so bad. And there was such a silence, such a long silence, that you knew the leather belt was on its way.

So here there's a wobbly table, a bench, a chair which Mammy sits on, and two big boxes. There's no carpet, not even a rug. But there's a gas fire, a cooker, a sink and a toilet outside in the back street. The worst thing is the damp; the cold air that gets up your nose, and comes back at you like white steam. The mattresses are damp, the walls are damp, and the windows too. It's winter, says Daddy, it'll get better soon. And when I get a job, he says. When he gets a job. When he gets a job! Why can't he get one now? This minute. Now.

And it isn't fair being a girl. All that scrubbing potatoes, putting them on to boil, and then setting the table. Tim and Gerard get in from school and it's, "Will you help me get the tea, Gerard?"

"No way. That's girl's work. I've got homework to do."

And he lifts his satchel off the floor and goes upstairs.

"Me too," says Tim, and follows.

Boiling potatoes warm up the room. But oh for a nice egg, or a piece of bacon. Back home there were always vegetables. You just had to go into the back field and dig them. Big dirty carrots, white parsnips and green, crinkly cabbage.

At mealtimes Mammy comes into the room with slow, heavy steps. Daddy puts the chair close to the table and she sinks into it, like a flat tyre sighing. No talking is allowed. And it gets so quiet you can hear Tim licking the margarine off his fingers and Gerard blowing on his potatoes. But then, through the stillness, you hear the lovely, loud tick-tock of Granny's clock.

IT was there one morning, and IT was a boy. Why wasn't it a girl? There are enough boys in this house. All those prayers. God knows that two boys and two girls is perfect. Now it's three boys. Three against one.

And you can't even tell what it is. A red face, slitty eyes and a wrinkly forehead. Baby calves are much nicer, even little piglets. They're pink, with a curly tail, they squeal and make you laugh. IT just lies on its back, arms and legs waving like a fat beetle that's been tipped over.

IT makes you want to cry. IT makes Mammy cry, all the time. But then she picks it up with a nice smile and starts blowing kisses. A good kicking is the answer. That will sort it out.

"Theresa, get the baby's bottle."

"Theresa, make me a cup of tea."

"Theresa, soak these nappies."

Jesus Christ what a pong. IT is like a pig eating, burping, slurping and making smells. Worse than the dung heap outside the old house. At least you could get away from that.

"Theresa, go to the shop. Theresa, do this. Theresa, do that. Theresa. Theresa. Theresa."

A week off school. All because of that thing. It's a great idea to sell him off. A trip in the big, old pram, up the streets, along the alleyways to the centre of town. There, on a strong box, you can shout: Anyone for a baby. A baby going cheap. It's a boy. A big, strapping boy. A big, fat baby boy. Going, going gone.

Gerard says that's stupid.

"We'll call him James," says Daddy. "James Patrick Lenehan."

Mrs Brown next door says he looks like Daddy. She's the stupid one. And soppy too. How a screaming, baldy baby looks like Daddy is anyone's guess. Daddy's tall with dark, wavy hair and blue, blue eyes. You never know what colour ITS eyes are because they are always screwed up crying.

"Lenny's got a baby brother."

"The name's Theresa."

"Lenny's got a baby brother."

"Leave off, Christine, will you." And a good push knocks her over.

Well, school at last. And the chance for some peace.

England, 1969

The stupid stage is wooden, clattery and loud. And in the dark there are faces. Shadow-faces. Mothers and children watching. They're down below, far away. And I'm up here, nearly as high as the roof. If I could just float away. See me go. See me flying out the window, never to return.

Don't know the three-hand reel. Never tried it before in my life. And my knees are knocking so hard that they're about to buckle. One girl didn't turn up, so I was shoved up here. Standing like a fool between two giants. The teacher's putting on the record. Jesus, hear those fiddles, the loud, scratchy music. And . . . we're off.

A one, two, three. A one, two, three. To the right, then to the left. And lift those knees. Higher, higher. Up, up.

"Follow us," hisses Bridget.

"Don't trip," whispers Susan.

Back and forth, round and round. Keep smiling, keep smiling. Head up. A one two three. Stop.

"Bow Theresa," says Moira. "Bow now!"

To get off this place. To be away from the slippy floorboards. And my poor, aching feet. A half-hour of toes squeezed into horrible dancing slippers. Already there's a blister on both little toes, and my heels are raw. By the time this is over the slippers and my feet will think they're one and the same thing. Blood and pus make a crusty glue. And when the slippers are ripped off! Mammy doesn't believe these slippers are too small. Now she'll see.

"You didn't smile," says Gerard.

"You get up there and smile when you're being dragged across the stage by two great elephants."

"Theresa. Come here. Your ringlets are falling out."

Oh God. Why did you have to invent ringlets?

"Now don't stoop, Theresa. If you could just keep your hair in place, you'd look as pretty as Nancy Riley."

Ever since Daddy got a job, Mammy's decided that real girls look like Nancy Riley. Just picture her. A face that can do no wrong; long, blonde, wavy hair, and flowery dresses that look as though they've never seen a spot of dirt in their lives. She's so perfect that if there was any dirt around, it'd be sure to run a mile.

The worst of it is that a real girl has to have ringlets. You should see Nancy's. "They're natural," says her mother, and on her face there's that look which says my darling is such a pretty girl. But there isn't a serious chance with my hair. It's not long enough. It's completely straight and there're hardly enough strands to make one ringlet, never mind ten.

"Your hair's a beautiful colour," says Daddy.

But what's the point of having "lovely dark hair" when that doesn't stop it being pulled into plaits, ribbons and bows? James has it right. More than a year old now, and still practically bald. Have *you* ever spent a whole day crucified by a plait? Or what about going to school with two flapping green ribbons? It's like somebody's tied donkey's ears to your head, and the ribbons are squeaking like trapped mice. Daddy no sooner started work than out came the combs, the two-inch ribbons and, worst of all, the idea of ringlets. As if it isn't enough to help with a baby, clean the house, and do my homework.

"Theresa, you're on stage again."

Oh, Lord. Mammy gives me a shove.

"Now remember to smile. You've a nice smile."

She's only saying that because it's better for *her* to have a daughter who's up there smiling.

"Keep your hands by your side, Theresa. Off you go."

"A one, two . . ."

Irish dancing was invented as torture. It's got to be that. Who in their right mind wants to go springing around a wooden stage, kicking their bums and keeping their body as straight as a rod? Back home in Ireland, there's no Irish dancing. Our cousins go to school, and that's all. They don't have to go every week to a big, draughty hall and jump up and down in time to the music. Or listen to a teacher that doesn't look as though she wants to be there.

But to hear the mothers talking, you'd think this dancing was the centre of the world. "Irish dancing lessons are so important for them," says one mother. "Makes you think of home," says another. It's when they sit round the plastic tables during the breaks, drinking tea and eating morning-coffee biscuits. All they talk about is who they've left back in Ireland. And how much they miss home. But if I went up and said, "And what about me? I left my granny behind, and the fields, and the chickens," it would be, "Whose bold child is this?" and, "Have you ever heard the likes of such cheek?" And Mammy would slap me across the legs, in front of all of them, and then she'd moan on about the trouble of being a mother, and the shame children bring on the family. So you give up, and just say nothing.

Then on top of all that, there's the mothers who act as though their daughter is going to be some kind of star. That they'll be the next Petula Clark or something. And it's only Irish dancing. It's not as if it's ballet, or something important. You see photos of ballet dancers in books, but never photos of this clodhopping.

"Your dress is too big," says Nancy.

"Is it?"

This is what happens when you have a second-hand dress, and you're around someone who doesn't think twice about telling you what you already know.

"You'll grow into it," says Mammy.

"Well *your* dress is too tight, Nancy."

"I know," she says, without a care in the world. "My mammy says I'm beautiful. And she's having a new dress specially made for me."

She opens her bright-pink case, the one she carries with her wherever she goes.

"Do you want a sweet?" she asks, and shakes open a huge, crinkly bag of Liquorice Allsorts. That lovely smell! The coconut whirls are the best, or the sandwiches. Liquorice, brown and pink.

"No thanks," I say.

Well you have to be able to say no. If you don't have a vanity case, or any pennies for lemonade, it's better to just say no. And you can always pretend that it's Lent.

"And the winners of the three-hand reel are Bridget Leonard, Theresa Lenehan and Susan Jones."

Well would you believe it? We won. If you can win a gold medal that easily, it's not worth the effort. Mammy's glad though. She's already lording it over Nancy Riley's mother. "It was Theresa that made all the difference," she'll be saying, "If she hadn't stepped in." Anything to let the Rileys know we're as good as them. Secretly she'll think what did it was the ringlets.

If God's trying to be scary, then he's making a good job of it. We're that close to the bishop you can count his eyelashes. And Father Kelly's to the right of him, glaring so hard this way, you'd think that one of us was going to make a run for it. It's not as if we could, lined up like white, frilly sheep in front of everybody. And there are all our sponsors in a row at our backs.

"I expect the confirmation class of St Thomas's Junior School to show Bishop Heaney what good Catholic girls you are. Be dutiful and obedient." That was in class last week, and Father Kelly was as grumpy as ever.

Obedient and dutiful. It's his way of saying, "Be Good!" and don't dare show me up. So we're dressed to the nines. Christine's dress has little white pearls, and Fiona's come in something plain, but at least it's white. If it was just the dress, the rosary beads and the prayer books, everything would be all right. But the thing is, I'm dying to go to the toilet.

Is God doing this as a test? It'd be easier if he came down from heaven now and just said, "Follow me." I'd follow in an instant. Instead, you have to last being slapped on the face by the Bishop, and praying for an hour at mass. And all this without making a puddle. Jesus, mustn't think of puddles. Mustn't think.

Standing's just about OK. Drop the prayer book, bend forward, cross your legs tightly, and you can last a bit longer. That's it. Steadier now. Make it through the next bit. Then it's forward to the rail. If I had my way this'd be done hopping. As it is, one leg takes a stiff step in front of the other. Like I think I'm the Queen of Sheba. Uncle Sean's come all the way from Ireland to be my sponsor; he'll be thinking he has a right eijit here.

Bishop Heaney's practically bald, and the little bit of hair he has is white. He looks like the hamster at our school, except his head's so shiny you'd think he's been washed down with a hose. If only Father Kelly'd stop looking at us like someone's about to commit a mortal sin.

"Theresa Mary Frances Lenehan, do you swear to renounce the devil and all his works?"

"I do, Father . . . Bishop."

Oh Christ, there's a spurt. Getting things wrong makes it worse. Mustn't give in. Must bite my tongue. Think of St Frances. The best part of this is choosing a new name. Frances. If I have a little girl I'll call her Frances. That's it, kneel and pray. Count the beads of the rosary. Say the rosary. Hail Mary full of grace, the Lord is with thee, blessed art thou . . .

No good. Can't last.

"Uncle Sean, I've got to go to the toilet. Badly!"

The whisper creeps along the line of girls, back to the parents. Everyone's heard. And someone's laughing. Well, just let them. But did Uncle Sean realise that badly means *badly*? He did. He's getting up. Thank you, God. Thank you.

Doesn't matter if everyone's looking. Just follow Uncle Sean, right across the church to the door to behind the altar. His hand's warm and he's so tall that it's as if no one can see me. Father Kelly's face is redder than normal, and he points to the priest's door.

Still holding on. Jesus. I can't make a puddle in the priest's room. Or on the toilet floor. Biting my lip so hard I can taste blood. Crossed legs, hop, hop, and hop again. There now. Door still open. Slowly, slowly. Knickers down. Whew. Oh, the relief. Well God bless my guardian angel and St Frances!

"Now, Theresa, was all that fuss really necessary?" says Father

Kelly as I creep back to the church. His breath smells sour.

"Yes, Father. I'm sorry, Father."

Behind him everyone is leaving. No one looks my way. Except Mammy.

"Don't let it happen again, Theresa."

"No, Father, I won't, Father."

Then James starts crying at the back of the Church. And I want to hug him. By the time I get outside he'll have made such a fuss, she'll have forgotten about me.

You wouldn't believe a tea cloth could cause such a fuss. But there it is, nailed to the wall next to the map of the world. It's just wide enough to cover the patch of scraped wallpaper above the side-board.

"Why can't she use it to dry dishes?" moans Gerard.

"It's too stiff. Pure Irish linen."

"Always the know-all, Theresa!"

Know-all. I'd give him know-all. I'd give him a bloodied nose if he wasn't so big. Just because he has to have the last word.

"Irish men and Irish women in the name of God and the new generation from which we receive our nationhood . . ."

They're the words written on the map of Ireland. About thirty lines of them. All written on a tea cloth. They're important words. Words shouted out on the steps of the post office in O'Connell Street. In 1916. When Irish people fought so that Ireland could be free. Makes your heart burst to think of it. Makes you want to be brave enough to fight.

It's not the words that are the problem. It's having to learn them. Mammy makes us stand in a row with our backs to the sink. You'd think we were waiting at the altar for communion. And then we chant every line after her. Like saying your times tables at school, or saying your prayers out loud. It's so stupid, all you want to do is get away. And you ask yourself, what's the good of all these words? These old words. Specially now we're living in England.

"I want to go back to Ireland," says Tim when we're on our own.

"We can't, you eijit," says Gerard. He talks like that because he's good at school, and everything's fine for him.

Every Friday night the kitchen's full of those words. They swell up like we're in some great hay-barn, or a huge church at mass.

"Nationhood . . . Ireland's children . . . In the Name of God."

Mammy's decided that we mustn't forget we're Irish. It's not just the tea cloth. There's a book of poetry. And a book of lessons in Irish. And there're records too. But we don't have a record player, so the records stand stiff and black behind the table legs. Hoping, that's what Mammy says, hoping for when there's enough money.

This week's too much. Daddy comes home so late we're all in bed. And in the meantime out comes the tea cloth. Every single night! You'd think Mammy was using it as a spell. Maybe she wants Ireland to appear in the kitchen. It gets to the point where you're ready to scream blue murder. But next to the sink you can see the wooden spoon. It's a new one. A great big wooden thing, good enough to shovel a whole dollop of stew. And it brings you out in lumps the size of a saucer. So we soon find our holy faces, and there's not a squeak from anyone.

Then it's on to, "Now children, show me where to find China?"

And then you can breathe easier, and let Tim point to all the countries. He's no good at school, but the map of the world is a different matter.

Mammy has a lovely voice, but she won't sing anymore. She used to relax when she sang.

"Sing us Kevin Barry, Mammy."

"Or Danny Boy."

"No," she says.

And you know when it comes to her, that no means no. But up in the attic, on the boys' big mattress, you can sing your heart out. And for once Mammy says nothing about the noise.

"And Kevin Barry gave his young life for the cause of liberty," bawls Tim.

"'Twas a lad of eighteen summers, which no one can deny."

"A rebel band set the heather blazing."

There are so many songs, that it gets to be a bawling competition to see who remembers the most words, or the most songs. On and on it goes, until the tears run down your cheeks, and you can hardly see a thing for thinking about all the Irish who died young trying to save Ireland. Makes you wonder what we're doing here since Ireland's been saved.

Then Tim gets on to the subject of Joseph Mary Plunket.

"How can a poet have a girl's name?" he says, "Everyone must have laughed at him." He never stops asking. No matter how many times Mammy talks about it.

"He was a martyr," she says. "He was one of the young men who fought for Ireland from the big post office in Dublin. And the English killed them all. They were poets, educated people. And they had no pity, not even for the wounded."

And every time it gives me a great lump in my throat when I hear about it. But the songs are the worst, they tear at your stomach. So you want to sing them again and again.

"I miss all the singing," says Gerard.

"There'd be Uncle Sean on the accordion. And Uncle Joe pretending to be Elvis Presley and Joe Dolan. You be Elvis," says Tim.

"No," says Gerard. And it's a good thing, too. He can't sing a note, no matter how hard he tries. And then it's the same old thing.

"Tell us about the Black and Tans, Theresa." This always comes after the singing. So I start and talk on and on without stopping.

"Granny says they were great lumps of men. Thick English thugs. And they'd come in the night, smash down the doors of innocent people, and take away the whole family in lorries. Then they'd drive them to the bogs, miles from their homes. And they'd prod the people with guns, or hit them across the heads until they were standing along the edge of a bog-hole. And the Black and Tans would laugh as though they hadn't a care in the world. Then they'd lift their guns and fire at everyone, men, women and children. Even babies. They'd all be mowed down and fall backwards into the hole."

"Bang. Bang. Bang. They were dead."

"SHUT UP, TIM!"

"Then there was the one time when they came to Granny's house. And she was only little. And her Daddy made her and her brothers and sisters sit on a long wooden bench near the fire. There were eight children so they had to squash up. And he put the rifles under their feet. And the soldiers didn't look where the children were sitting. So they were saved. And Granny says she remembers feeling the cold rifles with her bare feet."

"I wish I'd been born back then," says Tim, "I'd kill all the thugs, every single one."

"Sure and you would."

"I would. I would. I'd free Ireland."

"Sshhh, Mammy's calling," says Gerard.

And then it's time for us to creep off to bed.

Gerard's passed his eleven-plus and Mammy's like a stuffed turkey strutting up and down the kitchen as though she took the exam herself. And Gerard. Well, he acts as though he always knew he was going to pass. There's no point in reminding him of the night when his fingers were bleeding from chewing his nails to the quick.

"Now, Tom. Didn't I say he'd be a doctor?"

Daddy nods. He looks as though he doesn't understand what's going on. Or maybe he's still half-asleep. He comes in so late from work, and leaves so early that he might as well be a ghost in the house. The only day he's here is on Sunday and he sleeps half the day, and when he gets up for dinner he's like a sleepwalker. And Mammy doesn't even give out if he misses Mass.

"Your daddy works very hard," she'll say. "I hope you're grateful."

"We are, Mammy. We are."

But going back to Gerard. I can just picture the next Irish dancing class. There'll be Nancy Riley's mother and a whole legion of others. And then you'll hear Mammy above the lot of them.

"Well, I'm so proud of my Gerard. He's such a good boy."

And there'll be that pleased little smile. Nancy's brother didn't pass. So Mammy'll bend over to her mother and whisper loudly.

"I'm so sorry to hear about Danny," she'll say, and after a few seconds, "My Gerard's going to be a doctor, you know."

Tim's hating all the fuss. Gerard will go to the big school now. So Tim will be alone.

"I'm sick of hearing how brainy our Ger is. All I get at school is 'If only you could be as good as Gerard, Timothy.' Or even half as good, or a third as good or . . ."

"Ah, don't worry, Tim. You'll do OK."

"But I won't, Theresa. I won't."

And you have to feel sorry for him. He can't write well. Even though he's older than me and almost ten-and-a-half. All backward b's, d's and s's. They're easy if you know how. But Tim struggles and struggles, and still gets them back to front. If there wasn't James to look after, I'd have time to help Tim. That's if he'd listen. But, as it is, he's on his own. And he wouldn't ask anyone for help. What with having such a brainy brother.

James has turned out to be OK. Every week he sleeps in his pram in the library. You'd think he was the one who'd walked all the way there. But you don't catch me complaining when he's asleep.

The children's library's in a separate room. It's got proper books on the walls, and baby books, with pictures, on the table in the middle. They don't mind if you stay for hours. And we do, just as long as James has a bottle to keep him quiet. Sometimes Mammy forgets to give me one, and then there's only enough time to put the old books on the desk, and grab any new book. It doesn't take long before you get funny looks when you're the one in charge of a screaming baby.

Then the walk home is full of crying and whingeing. You can't help feeling sorry for him. Specially when all you need to do to shut him up is put a finger in his mouth. Shows just how hungry he is. But he doesn't see the people staring, and even if he did he wouldn't care less.

The best books are about Romans and Vikings. Then there're the books with witches and wizards. And magic. If only you could disappear whenever you wanted, and go to places where animals talked, and children could save the world. Like in *The Wizard of Oz*, or *The Lion, the Witch and the Wardrobe*.

Sometimes there're girls from school at the library. But they just say 'Hi'. Don't suppose they have to wheel a baby up and down the place. At least not into the library.

On good days, when it's sunny, and Mammy's put some biscuits in the pram, there's a great place in the park where we sit, and I read. And James sits up and looks around. There're birds for him to watch, and he tries to catch the branches with his little hands. Babies have no idea. But he could be worse. He could be always whingeing. Instead he smiles and lifts his hands to me, any time I get close.

Extract from
Mercy; Me

AMY HOSKIN

Amy Hoskin was born in Philadelphia in 1973. She is currently working on a novel entitled Mercy; Me — *this extract is taken from the first section. She lives in London with her boyfriend and dog.*

Writer's Note: Mercy and her mother live in a London suburb. Mercy is seventeen, still at school doing A-levels, and she works part-time in a garden centre. In this chapter, taken from near the beginning of the novel, Mercy's Uncle Gordon and Aunt Marie are staying with them for the weekend.

I wake up early and creep downstairs. The clock on the cooker flashes 6.55 — no one bothered to move it forward last October. Gordon must be up and out already, a grey skin puckers his half-drunk tea, and his newspaper lies open on the table at the racing pages. Mum is still asleep, I stopped outside her door and listened to her slow breathing. My feet stick to the cold lino while I boil the kettle. I tug the pull-thing and the blind swooshes up. Her radio sits in the window, staring at me, the two dials on the front like eyes and the mesh of the speaker underneath like a stubbly chin. I grab it off the sill, using my foot to open the door beneath the sink, then chuck it to the back of the cupboard where all the cleaning things are.

There's no bread left so I eat cornflakes from the packet. I pull my feet up onto the seat and stretch my T-shirt down to tuck it under my toes. There's a photograph in the newspaper of a man holding his face in his hands, the angle it's taken from makes you notice the bags under his eyes. The article says he's been a victim of police harassment for four years and he's forming a support group for other victims. I look at the photograph again. I squint till the bags and wrinkles slip away, and then I realise why it caught my eye. I know him. He was a friend of Dad's.

He used to come round on Saturday afternoons to help him work on the car. I remember their legs sticking out from underneath it; two pairs of jeans with swipes of black grease on. There's a dizzy feeling when I look at the newspaper then at the picture of him in my head, and try to make them become one and the same.

Gordon walks through the front door. I look up briefly; his nose is red. He claps his hands together and shivers.

"Hello. Up early." He pulls a chair out and chuckles, "For a Saturday."

"Mmm."

"I've been for a walk. It's chilly out there. Got a bit of a headache this morning." He laughs again.

"You fell asleep on the sofa."

"I know. Always leaves me stiff the next day."

I look at him rubbing the back of his neck, and wonder if Marie really did leave him there all night; the thought causes a smile.

"Eh?" he says, noticing.

"Nothing."

He holds his cold tea up and peers at it.

"I just made some more," I say.

He gets up and switches the light on then pours himself a fresh cup — "What you sitting here in the dark for, anyway?"

The light reveals a shadow behind the glass door at the foot of the stairs. Mum walks in, her dressing-gown wrapped tight around her, like it's all that's holding her together. She always looks lopsided first thing in the morning, with her curls squashed flat on the side she was sleeping on.

"Did you help yourself?" she says to Gordon, pointing vaguely.

"Yes thanks, Jane."

"There's no bread left," I say, but she's pouring a cup of tea and looking around.

"Have you seen the radio? It's normally right here."

Gordon shrugs. She shifts a pile of cookbooks but it's not there.

"Mum, c'm'ere," I say, but she doesn't move so I hold the paper up and tap the picture. "Look. Wasn't he a mate of Dad's? It's him, isn't it?"

She comes over, "Put it down. I can't see with you waving it around," and she smoothes it out on the table top. She tucks a curl in the side of her mouth and chews as she reads. Finally she says, "Graham Crowe."

"It is him?"

"Yes. Dunno why your dad was so enamoured with him. I think he knew him from school. Victim of police harassment." She laughs. "For God's sake, it says here he was in prison once. I never trusted him. And Richard wasn't exactly known for his powers of judgement."

"So d'you think he's lying then?"

She snorts and flicks the paper away. "He's hardly Mother Theresa. Why are you so interested anyway?"

I shrug, but she's not even looking at me.

She just glances around the kitchen impatiently and mutters, "Maybe I left it upstairs."

When she's gone, Gordon retrieves his paper from the far end of the table and whistles through his teeth, "I wouldn't like to be up in court with your mother on the jury."

I shiver and hug my legs, suddenly realising how cold I am.

Mum is down on her hands and knees in the kitchen when I get back from work. I ask what she's doing.

"This bloody radio. I can't find it anywhere."

I grab some biscuits from the plastic box and wander over to the back door. Rain has collected in the cracks where the weeds sprout from. The clothes-line I used to swing on hangs uselessly from its rusty pole. It never was fixed.

"God, where is the stupid thing?"

I turn and watch her rooting around behind the dryer and almost give in, but the phone starts ringing. She pushes the hair out of her face and sighs, "Oh that'll be for you, Mercy. Some girl, Suzy or something, called three times while you were out. I told her you'd call her when you got back."

I walk into the hallway and pick it up.

"Mercy, is that you?"

"Yes."

"It's Suzy. Where've you been? I've been trying to get you all afternoon."

"At work."

"Who's that woman who answered? She sounded pissed off."

"My flatmate. Just ignore her. She doesn't like taking messages."

"I was calling about tonight. You are coming. It's my birthday."

"I know it's your birthday."

"Ben got the stuff. I'm so excited."

"I'll be there, don't worry."

"Goodgood. Look I was thinking why don't we come and pick you up, we could all go for a drink before?"

"No, don't worry about that. I'll see you there."

She sounds disappointed. "All right. But don't be too late. I can't wait."

I put the phone down and go upstairs. Gordon and Marie are still out at his convention, so I flop down on the sofa and listen to the silence.

A few minutes later the sound of crashing objects below is followed by a cry. And then the crackle of voices surging across the air waves becomes a constant background hum.

I take a deep breath and try to explain again.

"Suzy is a friend from the garden centre, it's her birthday, I'm going to her house for a party."

"No, Mercy. Look, you said you'd be around this weekend while they were here."

"I came out with you last night."

"Oh well, and don't we feel honoured . . ."

"So what do you expect me to do tonight? I'm going out."

"You can be so selfish, Mercy, you don't think about anyone . . ."

Her voice is getting louder, she's forgetting that they're sitting in the lounge on the other side of the wall, and I know where this is leading so I run downstairs, only stopping to grab the rucksack from under the radiator.

"I'm gone, OK? I'll stay the night at Suzy's."

She follows me down shouting my name but stops outside the front door. She says it one more time, but more like a plea than anything else — "Mercy."

At the foot of the street I glance back; Gordon and Marie are shadows in the window above her, twitching the lounge curtains.

Earlier on when I walked into the club I thought he'd shaved his dreads off, but now Nick introduces me to his brother Mark and I laugh. Up close they only look similar; something around the eyes and the bones in the forehead, but a different mouth — and no scar. He says he's been travelling around South America and Nick laughs: "Couldn't handle the pace here." I watch him while Nick sorts someone out; he can't keep his arms still, though his hands are stuffed into his pockets. But when a tall man comes out of the crowd his back relaxes and they walk off together.

I sit down at the table and light a cigarette. Suzy is dragging by the hand a tall girl, whose face is screwed up like she's in pain. I hear Suzy say to her, "Ah, but it's worth it though," before she throws her arms around my neck.

"Birthday kiss . . ." she says, presenting her lips, then whispers so close to my ear that a shiver runs down my front. "Oh Mercy, these pills are beeeauutiful. Pure callies, I'm off my tits. Can you tell?"

"I'd never have guessed," I say.

The tall girl stands there looking lost till Suzy remembers and pulls her over.

"Mercy, this is a very old friend of mine, Delilah, who is here tonight under protest but she's going to have a brilliant time. You've got to help me make sure she does."

Delilah is at least four inches taller than me, with eyes like fish scales under water, and I think to myself that someone as beautiful as her will indeed be some man's downfall. But she doesn't seem to notice this about herself. She smiles shyly and sits down. Suzy starts fiddling with her skirt and winks at me, "Hang on," then reaches under the table and taps my knee. I take the pill she's holding. She jigs up and down in her seat, "Here we go . . ."

When Mark comes back I move up so he can slip in next to me.

Suzy nods to him, "Where've you been lately? We haven't seen you for ages. Taking it easy?"

"Yeah something like that. Been away, sorting me head out."

"And now you're messing it up again?"

"That's the one," he grins.

"Have you met Delilah?"

"Na, don't think I have — all right?"

She smiles and looks around as if she's waiting for someone.

He wipes his nose and twists round to face me. "What's your name again?"

"Mercy."

He nods and smiles. "Yeah, yeah . . . so how do you know my brother, then?" But before I say anything he points to his chest and goes, "Stupid. How come anyone knows Nick, huh?" then turns back to me, "These pills are serious," drawing the word out with glee, "calleees."

The rush is a pure long slide into heaven, like sticking your head out of a car window at seventy miles an hour. There are shivers and swells of something travelling through my skin. I keep shaking my head, making oohhhhs and sighs. I look around the table and can't believe the tender feelings I hold for every living creature on the face of the earth. Mark sees my shining eyes and goes, "That good?"

And when I think how beautiful Delilah looks the words just fall right out of my mouth into her lap, which I reach out to touch, to feel the shiny stuff of her dress. She coos to me through chattering teeth, "Let's go and dance." The music hangs like icicles in sunshine; each sound as clear as crystal struck with a knife.

We reach the middle of the dance floor as the DJ's bringing in that track with the best piano break ever and the girl singing of love. We're dancing in a circle, then doing our own thing, then bumping our hips against each other and laughing. "This is fucking beautiful," I shout, and all she can do is smile back. Now we put our arms round each other and kiss, lost in the good old disco sound of the track as she tells you what it is to be a woman. Then we turn and sing it to boys dancing near us and steal drinks out of their hands without asking.

Later I reach a stage of not knowing how I feel so when Delilah shouts, "Do you want to go to the loo?" I let her lead me by the hand. The walls are painted with shapes and words I can't understand. To suddenly be on soft springy carpet after the hard dance floor slows us down. We walk close upon each other and smile at anyone.

"Drink?" she half turns and points at the bar.

"No. Toilet first," I tell her, not because I need the toilet but because I've only just got my head round that. "You said go to the loo."

"Okey-dokey." She moves her head up and down slowly and seriously.

Now it seems deadly serious that we stick to the plan. When you walk like this, so conscious of each step, of each leg shifting air, each foot hitting the floor, you expect to be looked at. I have time to catch the eye of every person I pass and make contact.

But when we get to the toilets she stops. "No queue!" We don't know what to do; we expected a queue, that was part of the plan. She holds my hand loosely and we sway together, waiting to see what will happen. Then, I hear one simple synth line and forget that there ever was a plan, and my life is complete.

"OH MY GOD, NO."

She stares at me. Close to tears I take her face in my hands and tell her, "I can't believe it, this is my favourite song. I've got to go and dance," and for a short moment it really is life and death. I leave her and run back the way we came. The leap onto the stage is effortless, to touch the ceiling with my palms is a cinch, to die smiling and dancing seems like a real possibility.

I come back down to earth and tread on someone's fingers. I look down to say sorry and her eyes are flicking back into her skull. I give her a cigarette to calm her down, but her hands shake too much, so I light it for her. Delilah comes out of the crowd and climbs up next to me. We smile but don't speak. She is breezy and light, and dances with eyes closed as if she's more interested in what she sees in there.

Much later, or it could only be ten minutes, we find everyone sitting round a table. Nick's trying to get more callies off Ben; no one's interested in his doves.

"Look I'll give you ten more, that's all."

"A score."

"No way. I've only got thirty left. We'll want the rest later, and I'm not selling 'em to you so you can just whack on an extra fiver and sell 'em back to us at the end of the night when we're desperate."

Nick holds his hands up protesting his innocence, and settles for ten.

"Where've you two been?" Suzy shouts. "I was looking for you for ages." We look at each other sweating and grinning, and she tuts, "Oh forget it, you two are *really* fucked, aren't you." She reaches across the table for one of Delilah's hands. "Glad you came now?"

Delilah nods quickly, "Mmm. It's so nice to feel like this again," then licks her lips lazily.

Suzy turns to me, "I called her on Wednesday night, then on Friday at work, and twice this afternoon. I told her I was determined to get her out. So this afternoon I said, 'Not good enough, Delilah. We'll pick you up at ten.' And now look at her, loving every minute of it."

Delilah's lids flick over her eyes, each word is weighted with breath. "We used to come here two summers ago, Suzy, Ben, me and my ex-boyfriend Michael. They've redecorated it. It's the same but not the same. Like a well-known place you visit in a dream but the details are wrong." She points to my cigarette and I put it between her lips. She puffs but forgets to take it out, so I do it for her while she talks. "It's been six months since I took an E. The last time was a disaster — it was just after he left me. I ended up drinking half a bottle of Nightnurse and watching endless cartoons. It was weird, I couldn't sleep for two days." She shivers. "Guess I wasn't ready for it."

"Were you and your boyfriend together a long time?" I ask.

"Two-and-a-half years, but we'd been living together for a year so it was difficult to get used to him not being there. I haven't felt like going out since. I'm not ready to meet anyone else, y'know — for anyone to take his place."

"It doesn't have to be about meeting someone else. We've had a good time tonight, no men involved," I say.

"Listen to her, Delilah," Suzy chips in. "Anyway you two've been gone most of the night." She points to her watch.

"No way, it's half three, it can't be."

"It is. Nick said there's a party back at his. Up for it?"

Suzy's crashed out on Nick's bed. Delilah laughs and whispers, "Lightweight Suzy," as we pull her shoes off, then she says she's starting to feel a bit strange, so we crawl to the other end and tunnel under the duvet. I check and we've got seventeen cigarettes left; seventeen cigarettes makes you feel rich; having only one cigarette left seems too far in the future to happen. My mouth is dry and swollen so I swallow a mouthful of water after each drag. Delilah is chewing like mad and letting words tumble out upon each other.

"I was in such a state after I got off the phone to Suzy, I was sitting there going, 'I won't answer the door, I'll call her and tell her I'm ill.' Then I went through my wardrobe and nothing looked right. I ended up shouting at myself in the mirror. God, my eyes were so puffy I had to lie down with an ice-pack." She wriggles closer to me under the cover, a foot snakes between my legs.

"Have you got some more gum?" I ask.

"What gum?"

"That you're chewing."

"I haven't got any gum."

"Well what are you chewing then?"

She puts a hand to her cheek and runs her tongue against the inside. "Oh no. I always end up doing this when I'm really fucked." She peels her cheek back and leans over to show me. It's churned into a pink swollen mess; she pokes her tongue against a white puffy bit dotted with blood, and winces.

"You've chewed it to pieces."

"I don't realise I'm doing it. If you see me doing it again, will you tell me?"

"All right. But why don't I just go in the other room and see if anyone's got some gum?"

"No, don't go." She frowns. "Please, stay here. I can't stand being on my own when I'm feeling like this. I always panic when I'm coming down."

I put my arm out and stroke her face. The grey light from the window is magnifying feelings, is being caught by the corners of the room and offered up as a picture of the emptiness inside. I tell her she isn't coming down yet and pull the last pill out of my pocket, breaking it between my front teeth. She swallows it quickly.

"You've got to learn how to be on your own," I say. "It's a difficult thing."

"I know. Most of the time I feel like giving up and running back to him."

"What stops you?"

"I dunno. I don't know where he is. He just left. No one's heard from him, none of his mates."

"If you did know where he was, then?"

She yawns and speaks through the hand she pulls across her face, "I don't know." Then she seems to shake something off and drops the hand to smile at me. "What about you? Any lost loves? Any great secrets?"

"No, not really. I'm happy on my own," I say, and she says, "Lucky you."

There's a clock on the window sill, one of those Mickey Mouse clocks with his arms as the hands. Its ticking is loud behind our silence.

I finish my cigarette then whisper, "I've got to go to the loo."

"Stay here."

"I've got to go, I'm dying. You'll be all right, Suzy's here. I promise I won't be long."

She lies on her back and closes her eyes. "All right, be quick."

But when I sit on the cold seat I can't go no matter how hard I push. I try relaxing and breathing out, even turning the tap on, but nothing happens. I rub a hand across my belly; it's hard and full. I don't know how to make the muscles down there do what I want. I tiptoe my fingers across the skin and realise I can't even feel them on my stomach. At the sink I wet the inside of my mouth and the water runs off it like rubber. A smile in the mirror goes wrong.

I walk back into the bedroom and Delilah reaches out for me.

"Please don't leave me again. It was that clock, ticking and ticking and ticking. I suddenly realised one day we'll be dead."

I don't know what to say so I put my arms around her, 'cause I think that's what she wants. I know she's just spinning out, but there's no point in telling her that. It feels almost false to be doing something like this, but at the same time it's easy, and I realise how long it's been since I even pretended to be someone's friend.

The other half is blooming gently through us now; we eased out of the downward slope and then Delilah rolled over in bed and said she wanted to dance. We pulled the duvet up round Suzy, tucked it under her sides like a cocoon, before we left the room. Now Delilah is dancing with eyes shut, she looks dreamy and light, unbearably.

Nick is sitting in an armchair watching her movements around his lounge. The tequila I bought when we stopped at the off-licence is nearly empty; I dip my fingers into the bowl of salt, suck them, then swig.

Mark and his tall mate are chatting up a group of girls who've been in Ibiza for the last six months; they are suntans and pastel shades of Lycra. The room is hot so I open the window and lean out to feel the cold air against my face. There's something else wrong, though, like an itch you can't reach. I can't put a finger on it. A door opens across the way and a woman comes out. Traces of her dreams still bruise her face. Before she walks off down the street she looks up, right at me. I pull my head in quickly and shove the window down.

Nick gets up and goes over to Mark's mate, who's sitting on the floor counting money. He squats down in front of him, with his back to me. When he straightens up he makes a fist with one hand and stretches his back, then walks over and throws a wrap onto the low table. I leave the tequila on the window sill and go and sit down opposite him. I stretch my legs out, resting my feet on the table between us.

"Do it off there," I tell him.

He looks at me, confused.

"Go on. Cut a line the length of my thigh."

I shake my leg under his nose. The music stops as the needle hits the silent groove at the end of the track. Mark and his mate are watching us; Nick knows they're watching, doesn't know what to do. Ben and Spike put the finishing touches to their spliffs without looking at what they're doing. The girls on the sofa have gone quiet, are waiting to see what he does. Delilah suddenly stops dancing, opens her eyes and says, "What's happened to the music?"

"Go on," I say, enjoying the captive audience.

He laughs quietly. Slowly he tips some powder onto my leg and brushes it into shape with the back of a card. He licks the end of his thumb and rolls a note between it and his finger. Grinning, he rubs his scar, then bends down and sniffs along my leg. The tiniest touch of the rolled-up note at the end makes my skin twitch. I reach down and scratch my leg. You hear that someone was holding their breath.

"Time for another record," I shout, jumping up so quickly that my knee nearly hits his chin. I choose that old favourite with the sparse bass and haunting vocals at full volume. I'm in love, I sing but no one can hear me over the record. Delilah laughs nervously. I hold out my hands and she lets me lead her round the room like a ballroom dancer.

There's a row when I get home on Sunday night. Gordon and Marie left after lunch, so we don't worry about keeping the noise down. But right in the middle of a long speech, where she's winding a curl round her finger, which means it's serious, I'm suddenly so tired that a yawn just slips out. I clap my hand to my mouth too late. And then another one, so big that my mouth stings around the edges like a Chinese burn.

I start to speak, but my lips peel back, and this one makes my eyes water and her all blurry. She goes to say something, but I can tell by the quivering near her chin that she's caught it too, and we end up laughing as our yawns swallow each other up.

Eventually she says, "I wanted you to be here while they were, that's all. I thought you could . . ." She pauses. "Oh I s'pose it's not the end of the world. It's just you know how difficult I find her."

"I know, but she is your sister."

She pulls a face and sits down with a small laugh, "God, she is, isn't she."

I stand there in the middle of the room and try to work out what she's thinking, but I can't. Now there's a different look to her face, she looks more like I remember her when I was a kid. There are two separate people, her before and the one I know now, but sometimes I don't know her at all. She stands up and walks over to me, and grabs my face with her hands. It is just the suddenness of this gesture that is rough, then gently she tips it back into the light.

"Tired?"

I nod.

"Go on then, go up to bed."

"I'm all right."

"I got some chicken yesterday. Do some roasters with it if you like," she offers. "It'll take a couple of hours. Go on."

When I get upstairs, though, I can't sleep; just knowing it's there, waiting on the other side. In the end I pad over to the door and yank it open quickly, like I could catch it out. I leave it ajar and lie back down, so it's a speck in the corner of my eye.

The day it arrived Dad said he'd show me on the condition that I only used it when he was there. Because it was delicate.

I crossed myself. "Promise." I was six-and-a-half.

We'd known it was coming for a long time. He'd got a catalogue first and pointed it out to us, saying the words slowly and proudly, enjoying knowing something that we didn't.

"This one here — a Newtonian reflecting telescope. Mirrors give better clarity than lenses." He tapped the page. "This is the baby."

Eight months later the baby arrived.

He held me from behind, one arm reaching up to show me where to put my eye.

"This is the eyepiece you look through. Now give me your hand, no the other one, and put it here, on the wheel." He closed his hand over mine as he placed it on the cold metal and I slipped a finger through the spokes. "Now then, keep your eye there, turn the wheel like this," he said, twisting my hand. "Can you see it all coming into focus?"

I looked, but I couldn't see much. It was really dark, like space with no stars, or the darkness you see when you're dead, I thought.

"Tell me what you see, Mercy."

"Nothing," I said quietly.

"What do you mean? Squint your other eye, it's not difficult."

"It's all dark."

"Space is meant to be dark."

"No stars," I said.

He pulled me out of the way and ducked up to the eyepiece. A noise squeezed past his teeth, then he reached to the other end and flicked something up.

"Lens cover," he muttered. "Here, have a look now."

I crept between him and the telescope and pressed one side of my face awkwardly against the eyepiece. I kept my eyes shut till I felt the hard ring wedged in the socket.

"Do you see it now, Mercy? Hey? Y'see?"

And then slowly, very slowly, I let my eyelid float up and I looked into something beautiful — and into something that I couldn't understand. It was like when you look through a wet cobweb at the sun, dots of light looped together, strung on invisible threads, and then layered on top of each other, and each time I thought I'd looked to the last layer another would start to emerge, really faint then brighter till I realised I'd never get to the end, and the sky wasn't black at all but absolutely alive and humming with light; and humming in time to each breath I took.

His hand moved round to my back and sort of stroked up and down between the shoulder blades, then slipped away completely. I clung to the telescope, couldn't tear myself away. I held on tight and prayed because something had shifted and now it wasn't me looking out, *it* was all looking down on me; a million twinkling eyes winking down a tunnel at me, and now I was on the outside, not the inside, out there with all the other prickly dots of nothing. But then the sudden warm pressure, as his arm slipped back round me and he said, "All right? Just had an eyelash in my eye," made my heart jump, and I let go and fell back onto him.

The day I found his note I ran straight up here, sure I'd find it gone, but it wasn't. Funny, I thought he'd take it with him.

Notes on Jerusalem

HAYA HUSSEINI

Haya Husseini is a Palestinian from Jerusalem. Her work usually consists of dramatic texts dealing with the political and social dynamics of the Middle East. Her radioplay, Lights of Jericho, *produced by the Australian Broadcasting Corporation, won first prize at the 1994 Prix D'Italia awards. She lives in Jordan.*

Adham Tiro came and went, just like that, first in someone's dream, then in real life he turned up at the doorstep with a bunch of carnations in hand, just as predicted, asked his question, got his reply and that was it. The end of Adham Tiro.

No, says Khadija Smith, I'm writing this.

Write this then: Adham Tiro sold felafel and sesame bread in Sheikh Jarrah street. He was the street's breakfast provider of oven-baked eggs and dried crushed thyme. Door-to-door felafel seller pushing his peeling green wooden cart, 'Ashton and Sons' on the side, a Haifa shipping-box flank from some neighbourhood dumpyard. Pale pre-dawn mornings and the words *ka'ek, ka'ek!* stretched out in vocal frailty, sounding the breakfast alarms.

Fine, says Khadija Smith, the same Khadija Smith of Ferndale Road, Leicestershire and now veiled resident of El-Bireh, fine, but let me ask you this, and it's this she wants to know, raking my brain as though it's not had enough raking already: childhood memories of rock-hill Jerusalem, from cave-hunting to roof-jumping inside the ancient walls. What childhood memories of this tortured city, I want to ask, what childhood memories except those seeping out of the stink of my shrinking brain, my black box of convoluted images, remembrances that come fleetingly from a Jerusalem returned to, revisited after a lifelong exile lecturing on industrial plastics in chemistry departments, lab-coated in sulphuric acid-eaten holes, choked up on particles of nitrous oxide fumes.

Khadija Smith knows other things; veiled, veil cover tips flapping on padded shoulders with the light breeze of Jerusalem's afternoon outdoors, at the plush sloped gardens of the American Colony

Hotel café; knows that my memories are mixed, my mind disoriented. I have two, sometimes three versions of the day's events, and I wake up in the morning, not knowing where I am.

Jerusalem, dear.

What language do they speak in Jerusalem?

And Khadija Smith, cool, upright, steady with her pen and notepad, sips Turkish coffee again, leans her ear in the direction of the call to afternoon prayers, uncrosses her legs and mutters her brief holy salute. Khadija Smith, biographer, journalist, calligrapher, adherent, historian, and with so much of the pure beginnings of a garden-green, magnolia-scented, hedge-trimmed English woman on a cycle-path along row upon row of Georgian architectural delights after cold English mornings on glassed verandas, with colonial relics of rubber plants by the corner stove, where other women and men stand, sipping blanched tea.

She wants to see straight through my eyes and I'm here. I don't always understand, but I'm here.

Adham Tiro, she says slowly, significantly, was nothing more than a beggar.

That's true. He took children on his cart for rides along the rocky hill across Mount Scopus. No, he was a beggar then and didn't have a cart; he ran away from children and their taunts:

'Adham Adham ya Tiro,
diro fil sama diro',

whatever that meant, because you can't throw someone into the sky. And Adham Tiro would come back, not knocking on doors but mumbling under metal-framed windows the tragic story of his venture with the Arab army and the British against the Turkish beys. He stood lamenting his fate under the pines, framed by the Temple Mount behind him, the Dome glittering on his right shoulder and the Al-Aqsa mosque peering from behind. What he did have was a home and a family when the war began. He saw an opportunity there and gathered himself to serve the Arab revolt as cook, as tailor, as general assistant. He gathered himself and nothing else except a prayer mat and set off on the desert road south to Aqaba. He intoned his prayers on the rugged desert floor and stared glumly at the setting sun. He came back two years after the war had ended, never having found a single soldier, let alone an army, except the occasional bedouin who provided him with enough sustenance along the way. His home, his family in Jerusalem were gone.

Tiro? What kind of a name is that? The tallest pine trees kept him in their shadow, and when his mutterings were heard, we knew what that meant; afternoon silence was over and we could go out to play. Adham Tiro, pine-tree statuesque, bayonet-war veteran without the bayonet or the war and with enough instruction on a new way of life learnt from the godlike wandering bedouin who invited him to goat's milk, camel meat and camel-hair shelters.

What kind of a name is that?
   He was a Christian, so?
   Khadija Smith wants to bark, I can see that, straight into my face, the way her pencilled light-brown eyebrows meet, her lips unglue, her veil tips seem to flap harder, but she holds herself, remembering my condition, and instead softly, tightly:
   A Christian, dear, with a prayer mat?
   That's right. The first flickerings of pragmatic, pluralist nationalism. Adham Tiro, birthright Bethlehem, was a descendant of the noble branch of the family of Tayros, from the very same Tayroses who fell from Greek Orthodox favour in the late eighteenth century because they espoused all three religions.
   Khadija Smith snorts. Here's *my* thought: her name, schoolbook, Victorian British Council-scented, baptismal name erased, scratched out, re-dressed into flagrant idolatry of the prophet's first wife, name and duty rigorously applied, and look how odd, an unchristian Christian name, plucked from its blood-line ancestry, plunged into a discord of seedless labels.

There are fourteen tables on the garden slope in the American Colony Hotel and only three of them have people sitting. I long to see West Jerusalem, the European teenagers in their coffee shops, crowded half-naked, nose-ringed, purple-haired and jangled in silver and leather, yelling names, kicking over chairs, jostling each other in the narrow table spaces, sipping over spluttered laughter. Inside the American Colony Hotel is the historical exhibition of its founders, the hopelessly tragedy-tailed missionary Americans.

Black-and-white faint pictures of pale-eyed girls in white frocks, ankle socks; the Chicago fire; the first migrants; the first trading cart; the stables and the stable boy; the colony after the expansion; the new wing; playtime in the citrus grove. (And I swear I can see Adham Tiro standing by the crooked pine on the padded ground of pine needles, smiling at the first flash.)

Khadija Smith crosses her legs again. She says she's never seen his face in any of the pictures. She doesn't remember him there. Are you sure he's a real person?

A real person? I mimic her tone because it is highly strung and it fascinates me. A real person? As though the frustrated tremors in her voice weren't audible. As though her eyes didn't tell what she was really feeling. As though she didn't understand the silent street language spoken every day. Adham Tiro? As real as anyone, except how he lived, how he lived his life in the dream-time of history, sheltered from its aftershocks.

My memory doesn't last long, and it comes out in Turkish: Where are we? What are we doing here? What language should I speak? I shield my eyes with my hands, because when my memory disappears, even momentarily, the bright light interferes with the soothing darkness in my head that forms the only image I can muster at the moment of loss: a black field against a navy-blue sky. Next, I have to grapple with several shooting visions, different events merging cataclysmically into one. But, condition or no condition, Khadija Smith finally spews out her frustration: Look, it's your memories I want, not some crazy beggar's.

Crazy beggar?

And finally, calmly: You're not helping me write this, are you?

She's writing this but she isn't saying what I'm thinking. What I'm thinking is this: the cold and the quiet that came from the picture of Adham Tiro smiling silently in black-and-white watching the flash of the first camera. The quiet and cold exhibition halls enclosing glass casings of first stitches, metal axes, doctors' rusty scalpels, a tall, yellowed wedding dress. The Christians were charitable but they demanded loyalty. And Adham Tiro, retired war veteran of a war he never saw, standing in lament under the pine tree, crookedly encased in shadow, begging Ramadan alms.

The first flash. The camera had been fixed on him, wide-eyed and blaring light, and he hadn't known what it meant.

He didn't beg for long. Another call to arms sounded and Adham Tiro shot off in search of a war job.

Oh, lord, Khadija Smith is saying, sounding like an American; you do, you know — years of expatriatism, a borrowed culture and the strained English politeness bursting from behind padlocked garden gates.

Oh, lord. Where's the logic, asks Khadija Smith, where's the real sense in this? Are you — and Khadija Smith leans over the table to whisper with soft sarcastic vigour — tell me dear, are you reaping the harvest of this century's events?

Reaping the harvest?

Nineteen seventeen. Nineteen thirty-six. Nineteen thirty-nine. Nineteen forty-eight. Nineteen sixty-seven. My head thumps at the thought of the many languages I'll need here, Basque, Catalan, Castilian, English, French, Arabic, Hebrew, and all the different dialects in all the languages; Nineteen thirty-six and Adham Tiro took off to join the Republicans in the Spanish Civil War. He didn't for a second know the difference between the Republicans and the Opus Dei empire of nationalist, rebel, soon-to-be Francoistas; he wanted to trace his origins in the Ummayad dynasty that resurrected his Muslim past in the water-and-stone sculptured gardens of Granada, resurrected his belief in his family's Christian conversion, the name change from the Arabic *Turan* to the Castilian *Tiro*, from *bulls* to *target shooting*, resurrected beliefs in the underground mosque dungeons where great-grandparents whispered the *bismillah al-rahman alrahim* in absolute secrecy, then finally resurrected memories of shipped expulsion that took his ancestors from the desert shores of Cadiz to the port of Jaffa.

Khadija Smith is smiling. She wants to say, I know what she wants to say. She dries her sweated palms on her cotton dress. Fine. Adham Tiro it is, and a Muslim past is what you're saying. How come they didn't remain Muslims when they arrived here?

Adham Tiro disembarked from *La Sierra del Mar* in Valencia, leaving the shrill cries of the Republican crowds' *¡No Pasaran!* in distant echoes behind him and wandered south again to trace his roots. He reached Seville before the end of the week and fell into enemy camp. No matter. He was a *moro*, and a real one, at that. The nationalists promptly put him to unpaid work in the freshly fenced graveyards.

You're not answering my question, Khadija Smith feigns patience, resigned interest, and her ballpoint taps on the table edge.
What question? Hey, I'm only kidding, really.
But Khadija Smith's not looking in the right direction; her pointed nose faces north-east; I'm thinking that to look at the present you have to look down, not up, in, not out, and Adham Tiro did just that: he dug the earth in the daytime, while at night, whenever he could, he slipped unnoticed into the uncoffined under-earth of tree roots and pasty soil to sleep protected against the wind, in the fermenting warmth and moisture of fallen fates.

What happened was that it wasn't convenient for his ancestors to remain Muslims when they arrived in Jaffa. They went straight to Bethlehem, in-lawed the ancient blood-line of the Tayroses and that was that.
Khadija Smith doesn't see the economy of the situation.
They became wine-traders, trading wine for, among other things, the solid Lebanese cedar wood and local wheat. The vines that hung abandoned on twisted stems scattered on the eastern hills on their way to Bethlehem looked lavishly good for the ex-Granadians who craved to relive the taste of their ancestral homeland.
Ah.
Adham Tiro, however, returned to the port of Jaffa on an *Aliya* ship from the northern shores of Africa.
Oh, no.
Khadija Smith is having visions of drastic complications, a Muslim-turned-Christian-turned-Jew, but that's how it was: Adham Tiro had thrown himself into the embrace of the most ancient of monotheisms; from North Africa, where the rebel, now victorious, fascists had dumped him, Yahweh's word had made itself audible

through the mutterings of the disillusioned people from desert dunes to moist dungeons to the limestone caves around Jerusalem. Wandering nomads or settled farmers, the disillusioned mixed their whisperings with the Mediterranean's calm sway, and looking up into the dusk sky, Adham Tiro saw the distinct star lines of the bull, the all-encompassing, all-endearing, ferocious maleness, the compassionate distillation of Abraham's fertility.

Adham Tiro had no family left when he arrived in Jerusalem. Again, they too had moved on. He chose the street of Sheikh Jarrah for its wideness, for its old-familyness, for its tall pine trees, and settled down as a felafel and sesame bread seller.

Khadija Smith looks towards the restaurant courtyard and wonders if I would like to continue the chatter, the interview, I'm sorry, she adds, at a dinner table.

I hadn't realised where we were.

Jerusalem, dear.

Jerusalem was crumbling.

Here, the remnants of an expatriate Christian colony, invisible now. The square stone houses that used to be someone's, not any more. I want to say, I want to say, but Khadija Smith interrupts me, unEnglishlike, I think you need your energy. Fancy a salad?

As if salad would thread my memory, line it out, paralleled and precise.

But there we are: the historical restaurant patio of palm and lemon and fig trees, and Khadija Smith sniffing out the buffet: artichokes, asparagus, baby corn. Haven't seen baby corn here before.

I want to say this: you live in the in-between, between what you can remember and what you forget. Time isn't history, it's what makes memory dim. Which is why Adham Tiro — and I know Khadija Smith isn't listening any more — which is why he picked up in forty-eight and took the long walk down, deep, deep down, south yet again, but veering towards the Jordan River.

Khadija Smith, sitting down, says the soup smells delicious.

She wants me to forget. She wants a swooping view of the landscape of my memories, but my memories have been overfertilised and nothing wants to grow there. She unloosens the pin on her headwrap, tucks the wayward strings of hair in, draws the cloth tighter around her head and twists the pin back in place. She does it so the pin doesn't actually show on top of the white cloth. My attention is jolted but I hold it: borders, veil, invisible pin. My memory strings are strung so taut that I speak, nearly spitting, over the table: Adham Tiro picked up and fled with the frightened people in forty-eight. Khadija Smith nods, chewing lettuce.

But you said he'd become a Jew.

The thread is thinning, about to snap. Adham Tiro was everything. Adham Tiro would have been seventy-five in 1948, but he still picked up and went. He went in the direction of the abandoned villages, military closed-off zones, landmined areas; he went in the direction of demolished houses, razed villages, corpses pressed into the earth; he went tight-lipped and cragged, leaning on his pinewood stick until he reached the sloped vineyards, vine branches weighed down by unplucked grapes. He kept on walking, following in the path of artillery echoes and the silenced people on the dusk roads; in 1948 he would have staggered onto the Allenby Bridge, fear and hunger burning him up. Unbaffled by the prophetic mutterings of new-found deities, he found himself on the eastern edge of the Jordan River. He was from a scattered people, the newly scattered, the new dispossessed in the unpredictable diasporic twists of history who migrated into first, a wilderness, then into a bundle of new foreign voices, where the accents slowly took on a burdened familiarity, where the past was memorised in faint black-and-white bromides in cool and quiet prayer halls, into disturbed etchings of exiled imaginations, and finally into token sprinklings of namesakes on children eating Marmite toast on patterned carpets, whose tongues flowed foreign fluency, and whose bodies were captured in the effortless gestural imagination of a new world.

And what happened to Adham Tiro? asks Khadija Smith, straining her interest, her resigned courtesy; then turning her head dutifully south-east as the call to dusk prayer begins, her legs unfold, her lips move to the brief mutterings of ritualised invocations.

It's already getting darker, and on our left the hotel lobby swarms with tourists, journalists, one tall American actor in a training suit, and my brain feels warmer, uncluttered for once by the flash of images from the bright lobby interior. Groups merging into one another, slowly, at individual beats, then dispersing outwards, making space, waiting in the archways of entrances, of foyers, then inwards again, towards the centre, bodies collected coincidentally in vague clusters, in the accidental arrangement of shifts and motion, into the discomfort of suddenly magnified close-ups of features, textures and the fleeting brush against strangers' breath.

Well?

We move on, nineteen years.

To his graveside? And it's here that Khadija Smith smiles, as though in triumph or relief, but I'm not even sure that she's there any more, or ever has been, the shreds of my memory are piling up faster than I can collect: Khadija Smith fading with twisted smile, a fig tree flapping against a stone wall, a golden dome foregrounded by flat rooftops and television antennas, minarets and bell towers, solar heaters and water boilers. And in the middle of these images, a military museum, a showroom of glassed antiquities.

Not to his graveside. Not yet.

A few weeks after the sixty-seven war, Adham Tiro appeared before my aunt's eyes in a British cavalry soldier's worn-out uniform, knocking on her door in Sheikh Jarrah and asking her the way to the old city's Damascus Gate. He told her he had these carnations and could he give them to her. In her dream and a day later, in flesh.

Ten Poems

CHRISTOPHER JAMES

Christopher James was born in Paisley in 1975. *Since graduating from Newcastle University he has been developing two feature-length scripts:* Junk, *a film about antiques and opium, and* Windbreaks and Teacakes, *an old-fashioned take on love and flatulence.*

The Night Painter

Wary of the too early shimmerings of the cloud shadows,
hung in high resolution: six pixels per inch in the eastern sky,
and negotiating with considerable success
the powder snow in the waterfall gully,
there, in suspended isolation, steals the Night Painter.

Registering the two warnings of the hay-spilling clatter
and unwitting oink of the carts bound for swine-market,
he traverses the subterranean outlines of Roman villas,
and with one arm sweep, splashes a worldful
of orange and gold into the half-light,
splattering the bells and feathers of cockerels.

Pausing only to refresh with a three-mile line of mint dental floss,
and to return to the broom closet for ample blue,
he wades the sheer river, dove-coloured in the almost dawn,
and speaks the backward language of salmon fish,
their conversation only hindered by his slight Bavarian accent.

His tasks almost complete, the Night Painter moves on swiftly,
fearful of distorted sunlight in the prism of glass buildings
and that the yellow hummingbird will wake grey.
Swathed in the wonderful smell of rain,
he retires at last to his cot and dayful of dreams.

Drinking in Winter

The flat-stomachers sip mineral water
and discuss felonious petty theft.
They are erudite and articulate
and can describe exactly the rate of ascent
of the sun climbing over Anchorage.

The bellies of the grumbling nation glug beer,
their speech slurred
and thickened with popular proverb.
They muse above the muted rumble
of the de-icing trains, and bask
in the sun climbing over cold white Anchorage.

The fur coats in the golden-white garden
hunch over tables: growing,
gigantic mould spawned from splashed ale,
somehow surviving on the wooden slats of hot frost.
'It was a room entirely filled with people,'
a drinker begins, spreading a grin, fat with teeth and tongue,
each cheek a polished red apple,
'and that is part of Matthew's genius,'
he quietly concludes, then retires parched.

The wind idly thumbs a melancholy note
on the thin bass of the telephone wire:
the dull thud resonates over Anchorage,
and drinkers listen and squint, tipsy in sunshine.
'The year has been kind on the rosebuds,'
they conclude in steaming clouds of winter philosophy.

Down Under

Leaving behind the pastureland in long, easy strides,
treading the underleaves, on all sides the thick wooded valley,
we arrive at water, where turtles slipstream above the coral.

Strapping on our lungs, and with our hearts in our mouths,
we submerge, the bay closing slowly on the crowns of our heads,
and sucking furiously at the bit, there is a moment of hysteria,
before we remember and forget.

Drunk on colour, we drop down to the reef,
exchanging crazy, corked grins, and lay hands
on its living surface, our thoughts rising in bubbles,
cartoon-like, to vocalise on the surface.

Wary of the inspectors, the schools of fish open doors
of themselves, and eye us from a distance with respect,
always observing the courtesy of the water, before darting off,
lest they fall foul of a gleaming incisor.

At the risk of currying disfavour with an eel, we turn, and begin a
                                                        rapid
ascent, a fluid natural mountaineering, and finally break the
                                                        surface.
Thrown by the shock of light, we are smacked into respiration,
and drop our umbilicals; elated by ourselves, we are welcomed
back by the wind, reviving us with its gentle hand: a breeze.

Father Figure

Your study was where you hatched your plans, and laid
flat your blueprints, transporting them excitedly
to the bedroom, where they were carefully realised.
You hummed John Cage into the womb and customised the
mobile to play Brian Eno: *Music for Airports Vol. 1.*

You raised us as students of yourself, and taught us
versatility at an early age: there was no alternative
curriculum. You controlled our programming: punk with Big Bird
in the nursery and a copy of *Pet Sounds* for each of us
when the body-clock struck thirteen.

At Hallowe'en we bit into apples and pretended to fall
about at your split banana trick. On Christmas Day
you replaced the Spielberg blockbuster with a Truffaut
double bill: charades were always Defoe and Richardson;
at children's parties, we didn't know who E.T. was.

We went to school, but spent longer with you to be
unschooled: we learned joined-up writing too quickly,
and spent our lunch-break learning how to print again.
On my birthday, you challenged my friends to Scrabble
instead of organising blind man's bluff.

At the dinner table, it was all gerbils and pygmies, raisins
and microchips, feeding us knowledge with the Brussels sprouts.
I hated both; you would quietly explain that I wouldn't leave
the table until they were all gone. I slipped them under my jumper
while you fixed yourself another black coffee.

Each one of us was a wonder of your world,
built block by block under your super vision.
We were cultural attachés to my father, and we
expelled ourselves as soon as our time was up.

Iceland

At night I hear faintly the up-gush
of muddy geysers; the distant 'pop'
of a finger expertly flicked
from inside the cheek, and the creak
of summer icebergs, drifting
a centimetre a week.

Blocking a draughty window,
there it is again, an article on
Icelandic farmers, who in bleak
winters, must chip off the frozen
beards of their cattle, which hang
in December like great hairy icicles,
to prevent them from hurting each other.

And by day there is no escape, either.
There is Old Icelandic to master
and sagas to digest in chilly bedrooms:
like *The Voyage Of Snedda*, who,
they say, fathered a child in every village
in the country and could eat a whole
musk ox without ruining his appetite.

The Return

Clear the tables of clowns, and bring out the tragedians,
lean your head out of the window and call for horses,
for the day is almost upon us.

Smoke all five of your neatly rolled joints,
close the drawers, and leave the sand-blasting of the cathedral
for a time less portentous.

Flag down the trams, leave the strolling famous
to their anonymous leisure, and don't stop even to throw
on your overcoat, for the day will not be cold, nor will it be long.

Demand the immediate attention of the ambassador at the
                                        embassy,
and explain that you have no time to explain; buy him a ticket to
Southampton, press it into his hand and see him on his way.

Apologise for your briskness
and make safe your own passage,
for there is no time to be lost.

Dial up all those you know swimming at home in fifteen-
                                        thousand-
pound extensions; tell them to dry off quickly, and slip
into a dressing-gown, for dignity will be paramount in what
                                        ensues.

For all those you find drunk, boil up vats of coffee,
(make it bitter and strong), and sober them up with all speed,
for what follows will require a clear mind and a regular pulse.

Pilgrims, halt your progress and return to your homes, leaving
the catacombs to their caretakers; jettison any extra weight and
                                        dispose
of your traveller's cheques, or else invest them in some brisker
                                        craft.

Borrow mounts where you can, and if necessary, ride bareback,
for now is the time, if any, to throw caution to the wind.
For those in a position to do so, commandeer a vessel

and steer a course for the familiar, for strangers will quickly find
themselves awash in the returning influx of natives;
stash your passports safely and set your mind on one thing:
                                        return.

Bishops, side-comb your hair, fix your mitres in place, and take
                                        your
crooks firmly in hand, for now is the time to exercise your
                                        considerable
authority, and lead your flocks out of the urban dark and into the
                                        light.

Hold then, until the rain begins, proceed to common ground,
congregate beneath oak trees, raise your eyes to heaven,
tighten your belts and await your orders; do not all hold your
                                        breath.

Norfolk by Night and Day

Stopping off for strawberries at Stratton Strawless,
sipping warm orange juice from the carton, we watched
red tractors climb vertical hay, and scarecrows with hay fever
sunbathe, doze and squint for the sea.

Hands hot on the wheel, we passed cobbled houses,
with stones rounded by sea water, sunk into the plaster
and groping for the radio, cursing overplayed tapes,
we made good progress overland and arrived at Beeston Bump

mid-evening, with dim memories of the road, Godmanchester,
thick, hot air and wine gums, cloyed in soft clumps of two or
                                                        three.
The sun was ablaze on the sea, a burning slick on the water,
and we set about pitching the tent, a purple affair,

pummelling pegs with a saucepan in the absence of a mallet,
before climbing inside and drinking warm wine,
while the night softly overcame us, the dry earth
crumbling invisibly into the sea just yards away.

In the dark, the car cooled, fans whirring down,
salt crusting on the bonnet like coastal snow,
while to the east, great furry slugs lounged
on the cold sands: seals lolling happily on Blakeney plains.

Inside in duvet heaven, I dreamt bucket-and-spade dreams,
until awoken by the hourly rattle of the Norwich to Sheringham,
and so I watched her sleeping and lay listening to the waves:
the silence of the sea.

Oscar Wilde
(i.m. 1854-1900)

An exploded carnation in your lapel;
a tie fit for an eighteen-seventy-six freak-out dancer;
a generously tailored suit from Savile Row;
with silver flamingoes for cufflinks,
brandished like spurs at each wrist,
and a *green* handkerchief, coiled thickly
at the breast: you must have wandered
down Somerleyton, looking like a million guineas.

Your hair parted like the curtain on opening night,
your face jowled from splendid evenings at the club,
one would have thought your conversation,
would have made your cheeks shapely and firm
— like Dorian's — but you weathered in public, Oscar,
you shone over the port and clouded over in the dock.

Monet in the Woods

Soften your eyes, or instead, consider in rain, the special
freshness of May: the dripping bowers, the thick sponge
of soaked bark, the thread glisten of tendrils, and in the sky, the
sprung moon, barely there in the cyan pale, the bright all-ness
                                                of day.

Now consider the blackberries, jostling in the hedgerows,
the thorns safened, each with a single transparent bead,
the fruit sagging in fat clusters, gleaned by shrikes,
waning from the weight of their wet down.

Consider the flowers which splay in blue gushes underfoot;
consider the insects which bathe in raindrops and dry
beneath lilies; and finally the paths, muddy with the May,
which lead into glades, clear with green.

Now turn about and you are an impressionist,
short-sighted in the shower, in a scene blurred with damp colour,
longing for a canvas. Your spectacles lie snapped in the grasses,
streaming with water, the gilt gleaming in the daylight.

To Be Honest

It is getting increasingly hard to write close to home.
This is partly because my family is moving north
and partly because I feel more at ease ransacking papers for
                                        phrases
which 'freeze in the quadrangle until spring',
rather than recording moments by myself:
cadging a light from a commuter at Peterborough,
rash nocturnal visits, or jumping the lights on the Bluebell Road:
'Red means stop, Dickhead!'

Somehow it is so much simpler filling my canvas
with cribbed German and manufactured crisis
rather than recalling awkward jokes over
makeshift mashed potato.

I'm afraid a pragmatist would not care much for my work,
with its 'blue moustaches' and 'flared patchwork Levis';
he would dislike my lack of sincerity
and profound absence of warmth:
he would frown upon my fabrication,
the way for example I turned
a harmless day in the country with a friend,
into a full-blown 'affaire de coeur'
and a 120-page stage play.

Why I can't convert the joy of my best friend and I
reappraising the last ten years, on a shingled beach,
into poetry, I cannot tell you . . .
for I would sooner opt for plagiarising
a line or two from Pasternak's *The Last Summer,*
than tell you about the time we fell out forever
over a Walkman and a two-bit musical, in London,
in the snow, last February.

Extract from

The Protectorate

ANNETTE KOBAK

Annette Kobak's book Isabelle: The Life of Isabelle Eberhardt *is being republished as a Virago Modern Classic in January, 1998. She also translated Isabelle's novel* Vagabond, *and presents the BBC Radio 4 series on travel literature,* The Art of Travel.

ANEZKA
England
1997

I went to the doctor the other day, as I've had a persistent cough for some two years now, and people are beginning to think I've got consumption. He thought it was asthma from pollution — I live in a town in the west of England surrounded on three sides by hills, which gathers fumes and pollutants, he says, like a dust bowl. I didn't think it was asthma, even less so when I tried out the inhaler, with its arid blast of chemicals to the oesophagus. It seemed to me more like a device to administer neat asthma. So I went back and said, could I see an E.N.T. specialist, as I wanted to make sure I didn't have some noxious tumour squatting there which my cough was trying to evict. When the appointment came through, the specialist put a long flexible tube up my nostrils, which she called a 'wiggly worm' in a coy attempt to sugar the pill of it being a repulsive experience — as if a reference to worms could ever sugar any pill — and pronounced me fit. The cough, she said, came from vocal chords damaged at some point by flu, and then further damaged by speaking wrongly.

Speaking wrongly? I was a little affronted. I do not lisp, I do not stutter, I do not have a speech impediment of any kind, do I? Moreover, for the past few years I've been doing some broadcasting for a living, after finding unexpectedly that I had a good radio voice. This was particularly pleasing, since I'd discovered this quite late on in my life — when my children had grown up — and so it seemed like a piece of grace. In fact, a friend much prejudiced in my favour had said that I had a voice like a chestnut. It's off-putting to have people repeat praises they've been given, especially without a drop of irony, but I should add that it is the only natural gift I could lay claim to, and so I cherished it. My face fell when it was suddenly impugned.

The upshot was that I was referred to a speech therapist at a local hospital, who began to make me hum scales to find my right pitch. I couldn't seem to find it, though swooping like a trapeze artist. "mmmmmmmmmm." Cough. But whenever she said something I agreed with, I would say automatically, "Mmm," and she would pounce: yes! *that's* it, that's your natural pitch, stay with that.

The speech therapist was a motherly looking woman called Mona, neat and well presented, with thick ankles, and a four-square body. She had flesh-coloured stockings, good sensible shoes, and consciously tailored presentation and voice projection. She sat opposite me in her pleasantly clinical room, smiling, with both feet firmly on the floor and her hands laid symmetrically on her lap in the approved relaxed position. She was probably much younger than me. I am getting used to this, finding motherly and fatherly looking types who turn out to be at least ten years younger than I am. Does everyone of middle age feel this? I wouldn't know, as I'm a bit of a loner. I've never said that before of myself, and I don't know whether it's really true. It has sinister and undesirable under-tones, and it has always been my mother's most damning epithet to people, particularly within the family. 'He's a loner.' I've never heard it applied to a woman before, especially by a woman talking of herself. It feels like a dangerous thing to admit, and I'm not sure that it's true, but it's pointing towards a truth, much further down the line.

Then Mona asked me *when* I coughed. I considered it during the following week and came back with the reply that it was (a) when I was on the telephone and (b) when I was tense, particularly in a group. Whilst I was wondering whether the chemical composition of telephone receivers made them allergenic, she said, "When the tele-phone rings next time, let it ring one time more than you usually do before picking it up." Whoah, as the new generation would say! One of those small insights that genuinely affect your life. Reader, it works. By letting it ring one extra time, you are ready. You have composed yourself. You begin to talk on the right breath for you. You will not be wrong-footed. Like a tennis player, you are alert and relaxed, and ready for the killer shot. Why should it be a killer shot? Well, I am my father's daughter, and paranoia is his second name.

I used to think we never had a telephone at home because we couldn't afford it. Not many people had telephones in the block of flats in Crystal Palace we lived in for the first ten years of my life, so I wasn't aware of any discrepancy. But when we moved to Anerley and a small semi-detached suburban house, and Bill Haley's Rock Around the Clock began to blast Johnny Ray and Alma Cogan into another era, then it did become an anomaly. Even Lily next door, and Ernest, her toothless husband, had a telephone, in spite of the fact that he spent his old age lost in the depths of an armchair in the back room, his head and hands framed by antimacassars, like a Francis Bacon pope, without the authority or rage. Lily and Ernest had a telephone even though they had no visible friends or family or indeed income, being retired. So if ever an urgent message had to be got through to us, it could as a favour be winged through to Lily, like the brass capsules in the overhead network at the Co-op which would send through your change to you at the counter, and ping and swing when they arrived at the cashier.

The ding-dong knell would ring at our front door and Lily would be there, with her orange-dyed permed hair, her carmine lipstick permanently applied to the thin delta of her lips, her ample bosom covered in mauve crocheted cardigan, and her slippers on. She would cackle with ack-ack laughter as a prelude to every utterance, her beady and shrewd eyes behind her glasses countermanding any joy in the laugh. The hair, the laugh, the lipstick, the endlessly polished collection of brass hangings in her front room were her shot at gingering up the lacklustre world of Worbeck Road, Anerley, with its houses so wistfully named, as ours was, after some half-remembered but stymied sense of space and nature: Hazelwood, Oakcroft, Ivydene, and with its surrounding roads echoing the geographic anomie: Thornsett, Ashleigh, Wheathill, Hawthorn. Lily's laugh was an advance guard, a pre-emptive strike, and an effective one, keeping pity, presumption, and who knows what other things that I cannot guess, at bay. Some upper-class women of that generation, who'd grown up in the twenties, had small terriers to perform the same function. As soon as you rang their doorbell — pulled their bellpull — there would be a massed yapping, and after quite a while your hostess would appear, her feet clustered with leaping dogs. They also keep the ball firmly in the hostess's court. And who's to cavil? Women of my generation, young in the sixties, thought you should greet the world squarely and unprotected as a woman, with no make-up, no false coquetterie, no feminine wiles, just a good education and good intentions, and the world would be straight with you. But in nature most things are curved, or irregular, and have protective colouring, and why should we be different?

When our doorbell rang my father would start up in agitation from behind the *Daily Mirror*. His eyes, which oscillated continually from side to side — a condition brought on by the shocks he had undergone in the war — would look up startled and vulnerable, out of all proportion to the event. True, it was a rarity with us. No one came to visit unexpectedly. The streets all around were a fretwork of terraced, insular houses collectively holding their breath behind the token colour of the stained-glass half-light above the door. Ding dong ding. "Mary!" my father would shout in his thick Czech accent to my mother in the kitchen. She would go to the door and he would listen, tensed, until he heard it was Lily, when he would settle back behind the newspaper. If Lily were coming in with news of a telephone call for us, the blue eyes would flicker above the paper until he knew who it was. It would always be one of my mother's relatives. Very rarely, as I grew up, it might be a message for me from one of my friends, though I didn't encourage it. To brave the phalanx of loudly ticking clocks, the bloom of anti-macassars, the layers of dark, mute ornamentation studded with horse-brasses, let alone the silently smiling and nodding Ernest, and to lift the heavy, black, parrot-beaked receiver were more than my callow heart could bear.

"I think I know," I said to the speech therapist Mona, "why the telephone holds some angst for me." I suddenly remembered, too, that my first, and possibly my last, real love had said to me, "You're a telephonic incompetent, you know," and I knew now why it had made me so happy. He had spotted it, although I hadn't yet myself. He had made an accurate diagnosis.

JOZEF
Lvov, Poland
November, 1939

Why am I aching all over, and cold?

The dogfish of sleep slither back down to their lairs, and I surface abruptly, a fish breaking the waterline.

I'm lying against someone.

I'm lying, I'm lying on cobbles.

Ah, no. To wake into a nightmare! The courtyard.

What time is it, what's the time?

Where's my watch, did they take it?

Lie still, don't wake your neighbour.

I inch my hand towards the cuff of my greatcoat, and slide it in. The watch is there. I can feel it, through my glove. Thank goodness. My precious watch, at least. I won't look at it, someone might see it. It must be about six-thirty. A cold gruel of light just dawning.

*

My breath on the cold mist will give me away. Puffs of fear that the guard must surely see. My coat throbs like a bullfrog's throat.

What's going to happen why am I here what are they going to do to us?

The guard marches up and down the wall with the gate in it, boots clattering on the cobbles, turning on his heels at each end. His bayonet swings from his belt like a dislocated limb. His back turns, and I snatch a quick glance at the others, and brush the flaking green wall-plaster off my coat. They are keeping their heads down, though a man leaning up against the wall catches my eye. He looks like a student, too. We both hold the glance for a beat which tells us all we need to know. We're scared, we know the score and fear it, we need to get away soon. Anyone can be a plant, to catch you out, but there's something in the eyes that's difficult to fake. I sense all the others, a handful, are like me, on shut-down and red alert at the same time. This cold, cold sweat. None, I think, are old. All are able-bodied. That's a bad sign. We've heard rumours of men being rounded up and sent off to labour camps in the east. We've heard that each commissar in Lvov — and everywhere in Poland for all I know, who knows now? — has to send back a quota of men to Russia; forty a week, I heard. They're short of labour there, the story goes. If this is what we're here for, I haven't much time.

I will be done for.

There's no way out of this courtyard. The huge gates are iron-spiked and locked. A crude lavatory opens on to the yard on the left, and there's a barred door in the wall opposite me. Two uniformed Russians open it, look out at us, go back in. They're not soldiers — not the Red Army, though that is on its way — but they're in some kind of uniform. They can only be NKVD.

It was the uniforms I noticed first. Coming back into Lvov from the countryside, I saw the streets full of Russians in that uniform, all with revolvers, all with a bayonet in their belt. And civilians eight abreast and some twenty deep being marched under bayonets in the street. Criminals, the Russians let it be known. They didn't look like criminals to me. They were like us, except that we weren't marched here, just collared individually, or in twos or threes. I was one of the first to be brought in. I shouldn't have been out on my own. It was a mistake. Clearly! But how can you know what to do? How can you work out the rules when they change overnight, like that, snap, so fast, and always to your disadvantage? How can you know what's prudent and what's stupid in these new conditions? They spring up overnight, like the statues of Stalin that mushroomed in the streets the morning after they moved in.

I've been all eyes, all ears, straining to think what's best in the circumstances, straining to fathom what the circumstances meant. What is going on in the world outside, what is causing the situation we find ourselves in? We know so little. Is the West at war too? I've no idea. I thought I was doing the right thing when war broke out. How could I have stayed in Lvov under that bombing, with the Gestapo overrunning the town? Stanislas and I ran away east, sitting it out in a barn, where a farmer let us hide for a week or so. Until it was all over, we thought — until England and France and Belgium came to Poland's rescue, as they soon would. Then — well, then we came across a Polish motorized regiment with one or two light tanks, travelling, they said, towards Romania. As far as the war is concerned, they said, it's all over because Germany and Russia have just signed a pact that Poland is going to be divided between them, and the Russians are about to move west into Lvov. Already, the soldiers told us, the peasants are dividing up the big estates of absentee landlords, the cattle, the furniture, the land, anticipating communism. As for us, they said, we're heading for Hungary and then Romania, to be interned as prisoners of war. It was the only safe place. Take us too, we said, but they said, without uniforms we'd be done for. As I saw it, whatever we did, we'd be done for. The Nazis to the west, the Russians to the east. The Russians, who were supposed to be our friends, but now, suddenly, they were allies of the Germans, who we *knew* were our enemies. A Soviet–German pact, between the two arch-enemies! Goodness knows why such a thing should happen, what machinations beyond my comprehension have produced this situation. What is behind such a thing? Search me. Ha! They probably will, and they will only find my tram pass and zlotys and — no bread, that they have already taken.

What did I do what've I done am I guilty?

Is it me they are after, or am I just anyone? Is this just arbitrary, to spread terror and fear? They were meant to be friends and allies, but — well, we knew about the Russians, we knew what would happen, from history and from past experience. We knew that before the war the border between Russia and Poland was up to seven kilometres wide, and a ribbon of ploughed fields, so that footsteps would show up in them. So Stanislas and I ran back as fast as our legs would carry us to Lvov, not to be caught hiding by them. This is what I mean, how to know what to do for the best?

We soon picked up that we mustn't walk in groups. If you're more than two or three, it's considered a 'demonstration' and you're rounded up. But then, being two or three is not safe either, because we heard they grab you and separate you and ask you what you've been talking about. If it doesn't match up with what the others say, you're accused of talking politics and put in prison. It's very easy to slip up, especially as we have to speak in Russian. So we worked out before we set out what we'd have been talking about. "The electro-mechanical engineering class we've just been to." "The two-way combustion valve." "The carp we enjoyed catching last summer." Ha! Goody-goodies. But there aren't many topics that *can't* be construed as political, if that's what they want — and that's what they want. The only way around it is to walk in a crocodile. How ironic! We hated the crocodile until the Russians came in; it was demeaning at our age. Now, it's protection. If we're all together, all neat and aligned, nobody sticks out, and we look — official. But you can't forage for food in a crocodile. I calculated it was safer on my own, there was logic in it — though jumping from the tram was not planned. But I can see now I can't win. The rules are as slippery as dead fish in a river poisoned by flax. And perhaps there are no rules, only authority, only bayonets.

I'm guilty, I'm sure. Of what particular thing?

Of course, they didn't tell me. They didn't have to give a reason. It was just: "You, here!" and I was rounded up as I was walking back to the tram stop. A man with a red bar around his cap came and pushed me with his bayonet along the street until we reached this gate. *Oyee*, he said, "Get in," shoving me past the guard at the gates. I was taking the tram back to my digs, and I'd spotted a queue, a short one, some hundred or so, so I jumped off and joined it. It was at a coal merchant's, it turned out, and it could have been for anything — anything is worth having — but I found out it was for bread. I thought my luck was in when I got some.

It's probably the last food you'll see for a while.

They ignore us completely, as if we weren't here. No one thinks of piping up, asking for anything. I hear a tram or a car or footsteps outside, yet nobody knows that we're here, a gate's width away. They might keep us here for days, without food, without telling us anything, until we're too scared to think.

You're dead, or worse, if you don't get away.

More Russians are coming out of the door, going over to the guard, talking with him under their breath. One strikes a match on the sole of his boot and lights a cigarette. The guard leaves, a new one is left behind. He doesn't look much older than me.

★

Tovarich, postyemia, tovarich. "Comrade, please, comrade. Let me out," I whisper. The guard doesn't react. He carries on marching past me.

Try again, it's your only chance.

He stamps back across the cobbles. *Tovarich, tovarich, tchassi.* "Comrade, watch." I flash my Omega watch at him from under my cuff. He turns on his heels and points his bayonet at me. *Oyee.* He makes me march in front of him. *Oyee.* "Get out." That's it, I've had it, they can shoot anyone at random. That's it. "Stand there, by the gate." His heavy keys clink in the lock, the gate creaks slowly open, he forces me out of it, follows me, shuts it. *Tchassi,* he orders. I fumble to get my watch off. He marches back in.

I'm free.

RALPH
Prague
April, 1938

Ralph Dermot sat on the terrace of the Ambassador Hotel in Wenceslas Square, with his fox terrier, Pop, at his feet, watching the most varied show in Europe. It was an unseasonably warm day, one of those maverick days that heralds the next season. Although in Paris, where he'd just been, they would say the 'background to the air' was still not quite warm, the waiters had set out tables on the terrace occupying half the broad pavement.

"Would you say that this pavement has been *invaded* by the Ambassador Hotel?" said Eric Swanston, from the *Daily Tribune,* one eyebrow rising laconically, as he inhaled on a thin Czech cigarette, fixing Ralph with a deadpan twinkle.

Ralph fixed him back, and took his time.

"A voluntary annexation, I should say, wouldn't you? An *Anschluss,* possibly. A mutual agreement between the pavement and the hotel. The pavement is rather happy to be invaded, I should say." The men chuckled, and Pop shuffled round in a circle and rested his muzzle on his paws, content with his territory so near the rich smells of salami.

"You English are so damned languid," said the *New York Times* correspondent Sylvia Ames, a recent and welcome recruit to their ranks, if a bit politically intense for the average Englishman's taste, even a foreign correspondent's. She had just been in Barcelona, and had cut her reporting teeth on the civil war.

"You know perfectly well that when foreign correspondents begin flocking to a place, it means trouble," she said.

"Well, yes, we might know that, but the Czechs don't," said Eric. "Look at them milling out on Vaclavske Namesti, it's a pretty confident scene, isn't it? I mean, could you imagine happy crowds like this in Whitehall? It beats even Paris, don't you think, Ralph? I may have a Pilsner or two inside me, but I'd say this was the best place in the world to be at the moment."

Ralph looked out on the quarter-mile stretch of six-lane thoroughfare that was the heart of Prague, with the Wenceslas statue up to the left. Two lanes either side for motor cars, two in the middle for tramcars, all flanked by these broad pavements which the Ambassador and other cafés and hotels were beginning to spill out onto. Where were the people all going? He had no idea, but Wenceslas Square was always full of them, and as far as he could see, they simply enjoyed the promenade and looking at each other, like in an Italian town. Perhaps, Ralph thought, they aspired deep down to being Mediterranean. Perhaps Shakespeare giving Bohemia a coastline had given them ideas. Perhaps their passion, which he'd noted with curiosity, for bananas, came from some long-repressed yearning for the exotic.

"Perhaps I will have another schnapps, thanks."

The waiter cleared the men's glasses with the flourish of a bullfighter, and looked benignly at Pop. A dog was so normal, the waiter thought. And so English. With the English here in Prague, relaxing like this in our beautiful city, what does it matter if Herr Hitler is bellowing his nonsense next door? We have friends, power-ful friends, he thought. And treaties with them. Not to mention our army. He felt another flush of pride. With a trayful of empty glasses in one hand, his other hand deftly capped the ashtray with a clean one, touched them lightly down on the tray, and, like a conjuror, put the clean one back on the table.

"You're new here," Eric continued to Sylvia, "but you'll see, once you get out and about, on the borders, you'll see how the Czechs aren't about to cave in, like the Austrians. It's a quite different kettle of fish here. They've every reason to feel confident. Hitler's stupid, but not so stupid that he'd invade this country with its *seventy* armed divisions against his mere *fifty-two* at the last count — let alone weigh in against the fabled Czech air force. I'll take you up to Mikulov on the border, Sylvia, one evening at twilight and show you the ribbon of lights running all the way down the frontier towards Bratislava. They light up the work of thousands of men who've been digging a line of forts for months now, deep into the mountains, fortified with steel and cement and every kind of bristling new gun — *Czechoslovak*-made guns. I heard the other day even the British army are buying their Bren guns from Czechoslovakia now — apparently they're miles better than those coming out of the Krupp works at Essen! In fact, rumour has it Hitler wants some!"

"You're making the Czechs sound like warmongers," said Sylvia.

"Good Lord, no," Eric said. "That's one thing even their worst enemies couldn't accuse them of, having territorial ambitions — though Hitler is having a try, and, come to think of it, he *is* their worst enemy. He's concocting cock-and-bull stories about provocation to the German minorities up in the Sudetenland, but it's a pack of lies, as we've seen, those of us who've been up there. He's blatantly using his puppet Heinlein to whip up resentments most of the ordinary Sudeten Germans don't feel. But with Austria now annexed and Hitler's mad gaze directed clearly at the Czechs — not even the Slovaks, who he's courting at the moment — the Czechs know they have to protect themselves, and they're proud to, after all, being independent so recently from the old Austro-Hungarian Empire, and the only real democracy in this neck of the woods. Morale's pretty high here. The Czechs aren't about to cave in like Austria. That's why everyone out there" — he waved at the passers-by — "is looking good. There's real spirit and confidence there, is my guess, and for good reason with all that military back-up."

Ralph looked sceptical, and wondered how much Sylvia knew of the real state of play in Europe. It was difficult to see from outside, however much you boned up as a reporter, and she'd only just arrived. His own style was to wait that extra beat before saying anything himself. He'd learned that it was always in that space that you learned things. It was probably from living a lot with animals, and allowing them to complete whatever movements they were inclined to make. They tended to have good antennae, and sensible programmes of activity. He stared out into the crowd, slowly smoking.

"Aren't you going to object to him, Ralph?" Sylvia asked. "Or are you one of those darned inscrutable kind of Englishmen?"

Ralph smiled at her, and knew he was.

"Oh, well, I suppose it's an asset in a foreign correspondent," she said, "I just can't be like that, I get involved, it's probably why I'm only freelance and have to pitch and grub for articles to be accepted, and even then they always cut the most important, political bits."

"Come, come," said Eric. "Your self-effacement is positively British!"

The waiter was back already, with another schnapps and two beers.

"No, no, it's realism, I assure you! But my point, Eric, was that when we foreign correspondents flock, you know there's trouble ahead, and I still think that whichever way you look at it, there'll be trouble ahead. OK, so the Czechs have a well-equipped army, but if they fight the Germans, that's trouble. If they fight, and others get drawn into it — the French, the Russians, the people they've got treaties with, the British — that's trouble. If they fight, and the others *won't* get drawn into it — well, forgive me Eric, but for a small nation to set its cap against a raving maniac like Hitler is *trouble*, even with the best army in the world. And I have to say, I personally don't feel the least bit reassured at the prospect of Czechoslovakia's so-called friends standing up for her. Just look at their prevarication — objectively, now, look at it. Look at their track record. Who objected when Hitler's army marched into the Rhineland? Any of the Western powers? None. The place positively stiff with treaties, and we kind of cough and look the other way. 'Oh, Herr Jackboot, oh yes, do come in.' Who objected when Hitler annexed Austria last month? *Niemand. Nadie.* Of course, least of all, the Austrians themselves, so they had it coming. And then before that even, who objected when Italy marched into Abyssinia in 1935?"

"Aw, come on," said Eric. "The League of Nations did object, and there were sanctions, I seem to remember."

"Utterly ineffectual sanctions, half-hearted sanctions, feeble little mealy-mouthed squeaks. Who's in charge of Abyssinia now? Mussolini. Anybody objecting? Who's in charge of the Rhineland, of Austria? You know who. The precedent ain't that encouraging for Czechoslovakia."

She was strong stuff, thought Ralph. And she hadn't even mentioned Spain, out of self-effacement, probably, since they all knew she'd been there and had been well-nigh heroic. An aura of moral authority preceded her, like a scent, because of it.

"Not to mention Spain, for God's sake," she said.

Ralph took a bit of his salami and gave it to Pop. American women were different, that's for sure.

Eric prodded him. "You agree with me, Ralphie, don't you?"

Ralph gave him a sharp look, studiously overlaid with twinkles, at the diminutive.

"I'm inclined to agree with Sylvia," Ralph said.

Sylvia looked fully into his eyes for the first time.

"I think you're right to look at the evidence," he said. "There's been a lot of turning of blind eyes, when it's convenient. It can be the first sign of moral corruption, in my humble experience — in individual lives, as well as on a grander scale. It's a tricky one, mind you, perhaps the trickiest one there is: when you turn a blind eye, and when you don't. Sometimes it's the ultimate wisdom. Like with children, you've got to give people the benefit of the doubt, give them the chance to grow better, expect them to do the right thing in the end. That's its very civilized aspect. But if it's a moral shiftiness, to avoid saying the words which are appropriate to the action that's going on, to manipulate a situation to your own advantage without owning up, it's bad faith, and there's always a reckoning, further down the line. Usually a horrible, messy reckoning. Usually someone else pays the reckoning, someone who didn't deserve it."

Sylvia, who'd been nodding agreement, stubbed out her Lucky Strike.

"Yes! That's just what's happened in Spain, after all," she said.

"Mind you, perhaps the worst of all is when people turn a blind eye because they actually cannot see. Because they *are* blind, blinded by — well, heaven knows what, vanity, weakness, whatever — so they simply don't see what's right in front of their eyes."

Eric looked at Sylvia, and thought how odd it was that the smooth surface of an eye, merely a membrane or two over a hole, could say so much. How could little fibres and molecules express so much, in an eye? What, physiologically speaking, was going on? The Greeks thought the eye was a window to a real fire inside the body, he recalled. File and think about later, when this war blip is over.

★

They walked out down the square — why was it called a *square*? — it was an *allée*, it was a boulevard, there was nothing square about it. Pop was squashed between all the legs passing by, doggedly going this way and that to find a way through, his tongue hanging out. They bought a *Times* from the stand. There were more newspapers in Prague than in any other European city at the moment.

"D'you know," said Eric, "there's more German-language papers in this country than Czech ones? I counted them the other day: sixty-three *daily* German papers, if you please, and fifty-three Czech. That's hardly the sign of a poor oppressed minority, like Herr blooming Hitler says."

Ralph bought a couple of stamps to stick on the postcard he'd written for his nephew, Jack, in England. He made a point of sending him interesting ones, since Jack had been given his grandfather's collection, and seemed keen to add to it.

"Eric," he said, "look at this one, it's got armament factories in Pilsen on it, billowing smoke into the air."

"Aha! There, you see what I mean. What does that say then? Keep off, we're strong, Mister Adolf, it says — like I said."

Ralph stuck the other stamp on. "Look, this one is of old Masaryk, hugging a little girl. Have you noticed how politicians seem to have taken to hugging children recently? It seems to be *de rigueur* since Hitler arrived on the scene. Even the stamps are looking westward, eyes fixed on Germany. Coded messages winging out." He posted the card in the box.

They passed a motor car perched on the pavement, ready to be driven away as first prize in a lottery.

"Fancy a lottery ticket?" said Eric to Sylvia. "If you win, we could drive to the border in style!" He bought three, one for each of them. Sylvia had a brief fantasy of sitting in the deep leather seat driving over to Vienna for the day and feasting on *Sachertorte*. The Vienna, she suddenly recalled, that was now occupied by the Nazis.

Za korun, za korun, cried a man who'd spread a newspaper on the street, and was trying to sell chips of banana stalks. "For a crown, for a crown, grow your own bananas." He was doing a brisk trade.

The Call

CLAYTON LISTER

Clayton Lister was born in 1968 and lives in Norwich.

"**D**id I wake you?" she says.

"No."

But she's said it brightly, like I should have found that amusing. It's what everybody says when I pick up the phone. At any rate, it's what her friends are saying when they call. I must have told her that last time I called her. But I don't remember that.

"I'm joking, John."

"I know."

And then the silence, till "So, tell me. How are you doing?"

"Fine."

But already the knot in my stomach's tightening. Ordinarily I'd be seated — I want to sit. I feel I should to take this call. But the chair's in the living-room. I was using it, standing on it, to change the light-bulb for the one here in the passage — if we ever kept spares I've no idea where.

I could ask her now. But there's a photograph framed in glass that's catching my reflection — what little light there is that's falling through the window above the front door there. She took that picture — Sammy, his second birthday, only two days before the accident. I didn't want it up there, any of them in any of the rooms, but she insisted. And well, I thought, if that's what she needs, who am I to say? What was that, four months ago, five? Only five months ago.

"Well," she says.

And "Well," I say.

And then she's sighing. I know how difficult this is for her — and wasn't it me? Didn't I ask? I said I wanted her to call, and keep calling. She's lighting up a cigarette now — the match flares, and she's blowing it out.

"What was that?" she says.

"I said, How are *you*? Are you well?"

"I'm fine," she says. "Roger's flown up to Edinburgh for a couple of days, so I have the place to myself. It's kind of nice, you know, to sprawl? It's not quite home yet for me, but, well, we're getting there."

"Things still good then? Between you, I mean."

"Oh, yeah, really. Fine. He wanted me to go with him. I've always said I wanted to, haven't I though? But it's nice, you know? To have the space. Things are usually so hectic here with all the people he has round, so . . . anyway, it's nice. And I've started reading again — really. That book you sent me, *The Child in Time*? Oh no, no — not that one, the other one. What is it now? I don't know — the other one. I am though, I'm reading. And you?"

"Yeah. Yeah."

"And *writing*, are you *writing* yet? You know you really have got to get down to it, John — I've been saying. And Roger *knows* people, you know? Not just art people. So do, make the most of him, you must. Send him something — just the other night he said that. We were talking. Oh, and, uh, did I tell you about Ronnie? The guy with the gallery? He's got my portfolio — saw some of my pictures here that Roger's hung, and *asked* to see it. Roger didn't even have to say. He's talking about an exhibition all of my own. Not till the summer, but still."

"That's great," I say — and really, it is. I'm thinking that. She's told me already, but still. "That's great."

"So will you?"

"What?"

"Send him something."

"Oh."

I've never before looked so closely at this picture. Ordinarily you wouldn't have to. In it, Sammy's swinging — the playground over at Palmer Park. But you mightn't even know that if you hadn't been there when the picture was taken. I think in the original there must have been a lot more captured than just Sammy, but she's had it blown up, then cut the blow-up down, so his face fills the frame almost entirely — whatever else there was behind him you can't make out. There's nothing. Just him, laughing. And my own face reflected in the glass.

"John?"

I've no idea what I should be saying. I say, "Which pictures?"

"What?"

"Uh — which pictures? Of yours that Roger's hung?"

"You haven't seen them," she says. "New ones."

And then that silence again. But I know how much she hates that. So I'm clearing my throat.

"John?"

"I'm here."

But her voice has softened a little just saying that, pronouncing my name. That's better, I think — more the Laura I know. This new way she has of speaking, of cramming all the words she can into as short a period of time as possible, I don't know who she is when she speaks that way. I'd like to point that out to her, ask her: *Remember, Laur', how it used to be me the one you'd be telling ease off? Give others a chance to speak?* She didn't have to say, just a look would do: *John, enough!* — I'd get it. But to say that now. She has a temper too, which is also something new — that just the kind of thing that provokes it: *Laur', do you remember when . . .?*

Last time we spoke, I called her: *You never wanted to talk about any of this before! Why now?* shouting, screaming hysterically, and crying — which I've never known her do ever, even at the funeral. We neither of us did. And then Roger'd taken the receiver off her, and he is, he's a good guy, I know that, and he will work wonders for her career, but that knot just tightening that way it can: *John, I'm going to hang up now, OK? Are you there? Maybe Laura will call you later, OK, John? Later.*

No, we don't want another scene like that — at any cost, is what I'm thinking.

But she's saying, "John? What does it matter which pictures? You haven't seen them. They're of Brompton, OK? It's where we met. . ."

I know that though — she doesn't have to tell me that again, how she had just found herself there, all the way from that pokey little flat she'd got herself south of the river she'd not even been in that long then; and Roger, nearby in his not-so-pokey flat in Belgravia, just taking a *stroll through the condoms*, he'd quipped, had seen her, introduced himself, and would she like to join them for lunch, he and some painter friend of his — if the condoms hadn't put her off? Laura, though, choosing London in the first place!

But you need the space, John, she'd said, *Probably more than me.* And me believing her: *A temporary thing,* first off; *I just don't know,* then, *Just a little longer;* then of course, inevitably, *I'm just so much more myself here, John.* Roger had appeared. Brompton, though, for God's sake — what, Laur', did your eyes lock over a headstone? *Oh, it's just so beautiful there, though, so quiet, and right in the middle of the city where you'd least expect it.*

"I'd like to see those pictures," I say.

And then again the silence, though coming more from her than me this time. I wasn't hinting, I wasn't suggesting I visit. I know, I remember, what happened last time I asked, so say anything, I'm thinking.

"You remember that day, Laur', when we were at the park, Palmer, here in Reading — Sammy on the swing?"

"Oh, Jesus," she says.

"Laur'? Did we have a good time that day, or what?"

"You're looking at that photograph," she says.

"He's laughing, Laur'."

"John, stop."

"You remember? It was his birthday?"

"Stop, I said."

"His cake you made, and the candles?"

"John, stop it now! Just stop it."

"He couldn't blow them out?"

"OK, that's it. I'm going, I'm hanging up, John —"

"And then at the park —"

"You hear me, John? I'm gone."

But she's not. She's there still — I know it: there's her breathing. Then, only when she's sure I have stopped, another cigarette. Which is also a new thing. Though she used to smoke pre-Sam; gave up just like that when she conceived. Before she had the test even. Which was how I guessed.

"Are you there?"

"I'm here."

"John," she says. "Please. Please, don't be that way."

Don't be that way, though — what way? *Don't be this way . . . that way . . .* Which way should I be then, Laur'? How would you have me be? How can I be? *Talk about it; don't. Use it* — you even told me *Use it* for God's sake. What does that mean, *Use it*? Set a story in a cemetery; two people meet . . .?

"Are you seeing people?" she says. "Have you seen Brian? What about Vanessa? Call them, John — do. You said they've been calling you. Haven't they?"

They're all her friends, though. Yours, Laur', you know? Not mine. This is your town, your family that's so close by; this where you wanted to be — isn't it, though? How *can* I be that's not *This way* or *That way*? There is no way, whatever I do. I moved here to be with you, didn't I? *From* London? I put things on hold I wanted for myself like you. I got up in the night, I fed him, I changed those nappies too. I mightn't have taken the fucking pictures, but I pushed the swing, Laur'. I pushed the fucking swing.

"I'm going," I say.

"What?"

"I have to go."

"Now, John?"

"I'm going, Laur'," I say. "I have to go. The kettle's boiling."

"John, listen, OK, take those pictures down. Do you hear? Take them down, and put them in a drawer. Burn them or something — no don't do that. Just — I'm sorry, OK? I'm sorry I put them up when you didn't want them up. John? Take them down, OK? Take them down, John."

That's what she's saying as I hang up.

And when I do, it's like that knot in my stomach unravels, just a little — but enough; I can breathe again — deep breaths is what it takes.

But when I look again, he's staring right at me still, or through me it's like, like I'm the ghost. And even leaning in close, still he can't see me — whatever the distance. I could move in closer still, rest my head on the glass between us, but still no. I could say his name even, right into his face like this, lips touching; I could be calling out his name.

I don't know how long for — but it's dark now, completely. When I pull away there's nothing you can see. But this bulb in my hand still. I don't know now, I can't remember, is this the one that's blown, or is this the good one? I'm going to have to feel my way into the living-room. How can I climb on the chair and fit it in the dark, though?

I may just have to settle on the sofa for the night, fall into a deep sleep there. That'd be good, I think, to sleep — wherever; and in the morning, come daylight, there be a call for me, and, bleary still but coming to, answer *Yes . . . you woke me.*

Ten Poems

Esther Morgan *is 27 and started writing poetry four years ago whilst working as a volunteer guide at Dove Cottage, Wordsworth's house in Grasmere, Cumbria.*

Avocados

I like the way they fit the palm,
their plump Buddha weight,
the sly squeeze for ripeness,
the clean slit of the knife,
the soft suck
as you twist the halves apart,
the thick skin peeling easily.
Naked, they're slippery as soap.

I serve them for myself,
sliced and fanned
on white bone china,
glistening with olive oil,
or I fill the smooth hollow
with sharp vinaigrette,
scooping out
the pale, buttery flesh.

Every diet you've ever read
strictly forbids them.

Bully for You

We are the girls who used tongues,
who learnt the grammar of boys early.
They dipped their liquorice into our sherbet.
We chewed our secret like bubble gum,
blowing it up till it popped in your face.
We stuck the hard lumps under the desks,
teeth marks still in them. Love bites on necks.

We are the girls who nicked stuff from Woolies,
picking on you, stopping your gob.
We faked ID and mixed our drinks.
Sticky as cocktails and just as lethal.
Sex opened up like a paper umbrella.
We were sick in the bogs, kissed and made-up —
cherryade lipstick, back-combed hair.

You were so set-square — all right angles
and answers, clever inky fingers,
your sly stare at our non-reg knickers.
We gave you Chinese burns to wear
round your spindly wrists. Root-cracked
asphalt bit deep into your knees.
Our jabs were scabby as rubella.

You dug dirt from the playground wall,
told our fortunes to yourself —
fat at thirty; thick as white bread;
the sort of tarts who shop in slippers,
skimpy T-shirts and no bras;
whose skin peels from big, red shoulders;
who don't have children but brats.

Perhaps you're right — though we still make you blush
pulling faces out the back ends of buses.
Your future's sewn up, neat as a name tag.
So why do the years gang up, link arms
like girls and turn their backs on you?
Life still swamps you, flapping round your ankles —
the school coat you never quite grew into.

Condemned

'Neither do I condemn thee: go, and sin no more.'
St John, Ch. 8, v. 1-11

Since then, I stay indoors,
keep a slut's house — greasy plates,
wine sediment crusted in cups.
I let the fire go out.
I'm still smeared between the legs.
He won't speak — or if he does,
my name's unleashed
from the sling of his voice.
The swineherd savours
the new wine of scorn
as he tips the swill out.
Trees hug their shadows tight.
Prostitutes cross the street.

The women thread bone needles of gossip.
At night they lay bad things at my doorstep
like a cat's cruel offerings —
a harelip, a young boy's twisted foot,
an old woman's eyes like milky stones.
The lover, whose unexpected touch
once made my belly wince,
clenches fists at me. I dream of us
behind the lattice screen — arid afternoons,
the shadows of carved leaves
filigreed across our skin. Something else
was dragged into the light that day.
The men are still afraid of it.

Passover. We prepare in ritual silence.
My husband slits the lamb's throat,
the one I nursed by hand,
talked to for hours in the fold.
He daubs blood on the gate-post.
Roast meat spits at me from the fire.
I knead the bread which will not rise,
crush the bitter herbs.
Tonight, I lie awake,
my spine curved from his,
listening for the rush of wings
over the face of the earth,
the mothers wailing in the wilderness,

and I wonder where he is,
this night of our deliverance.
Has he left others like me,
struggling to live with miracles —
like learning to walk again,
only painful this time, crippled,
with no one there to lift you from the dirt?
I heard the crowd parted for him like a sea,
spread torn palm leaves at his feet.
I would not hurl hosannas at his head.
Another dawn breaks red
like an unhealed wound. My eyes bloom,
dark as bruises on the world.

Relics

The causeway is a fine thread
tying the island to the mainland shore;
a fragile mooring cut twice a day by tides.
It feels like an act of faith as we set foot
on this narrow parting of the North Sea.

Holy Island. Seagulls' sanctuary.
The endless keening of the birds.
Life lived close-cropped like turf.
Monks kneel in our minds stiff as stone
with worship, intoning salt prayers.

Battling along the beach, heads bent
past the stranded hulls of upturned boats
we fight to breathe, like fish,
hooked and flapping,
slapped dead on the wet decks.

The ruined priory still does penance,
wind-whipped, strafed by sand, roofless
but for one communicating arch,
whittled thin as bone, which leaps
the gulf between two massive pillars.

A small victory as you light a cigarette
cupping your hands to protect the flame.
Your voice takes shelter in my name
as you slip your hand to share my pocket's warmth.
The sun sets in a streak of gold leaf

lending sandstone a brief radiance.
We exchange gritted kisses in the failing light
then turn to beat the tide back home.
Behind us the Rainbow Arch is inked against the sky
braced to carry the weight of one more night.

The Sinking of HMS Repulse, December 1941

From the Air Defence Control Tower
170 ft above the deck,
Midshipman Peter Gillis, aged 18,
looks down on the crippled ship.
The tiny figures of the crew
swarm amongst the fires and smoke.

Men are leaping overboard.
One jumps too far aft
and is sucked into the propeller.
A boy on the observation post below
hits the rail, breaks his back,
and crumples into the sea.
Another takes aim, misses,
and shoots straight down the smokestack.

He unlaces his boots, easing them free.
They're new — navy issue,
heavy-duty leather.
They would have worn well.
He tucks them neatly together
as though getting ready for bed.

Dirty Water

Mid-afternoon. I lock the door
and run a deep bath. Into the water
I drop an iridescent pearl.
The seam splits, releasing slick oil.
I slide in — a slight gasp
then aaaahh . . .
slowly, all my muscles uncoil.
The flap of pearl skin's floating.
I begin rubbing it between my fingers.
It is slippery, gradually dissolving . . .

The sudden slap of a ladder against the wall.
I wince like an opened oyster.
A wiper blade flicks suds across the pane.
A blurred face stares through frosted glass.
My fingertips shrivel before the last,
sharp line of soap is squeaked clean.
I pull the plug, the dirty water drains,
my body grows heavier, colder . . .
Downstairs, mother opens the back door.
She is paying him.

Last Supper

Notebooks out. You're taking my order.
I'll have steak cooked bloody
and apple pie like Ma
never used to make. Cunt.
Sorry. C***. No offence.
I get special treatment.
The meat's been cut
into neat bite-sized chunks.
Plastic kiddy fork. Thoughtful.
First decent meal in months.
No appetite, but I eat it all up.
I'm a strapping guy. A good raw boy.
You want to chew the cold fat over?

My mother's maggoty white toes
in their slickety-slack sandals
went creeping up my spine.
How's that for starters? Satisfied?
You want *all* the juicy stuff?
I was the apple of her bloodshot eye.
She was clinging as syrup peaches
sliding from the jagged can.
Sloppy as melted ice-cream.
I scooped her out. Raspberry blood.
I topped my mothering sundae
with whipped cream and dreams
chopped like nuts. Just desserts.

I like my girls lean.
The grind of bone on bone.
Tough but tender. I treated myself once.
She was my girl lollipop, licked up sticky.
I was her young blade
sliding between pink-jelly thighs.
All I did was tickle her ribs,
hit her funny bone, twist her arm

a little bit — no harm meant.
I see her now — the black O
of her mouth like laughter.
I don't recall exactly how. Something
snapped, got stuck in her throat.

Tonight I'm hard and split-pea dried,
rattling in my empty pod. The priest
gushes God like a Sodastream.
There's a mean-looking moon
like the slit of a narrowed eye.
The radio's broke. Snatches of tunes —
Bye, bye Miss American Pie
Voices fading in and out of the dark
like passing cars, the fierce
crackle and hiss of silence —
static in my head, as if the stars
are frying up there
in the big, black pan of the sky.

The dawn's grubby-mac grey
and dripping dirty rain.
Outside, I'm allowed a cigarette.
The mob's baying at the gates.
I read the health warning,
and drag on these seconds right down
to the last nicotine-stained butt.
I double up, cramp skewering my guts.
'Indigestion?' Sick jokes.
A quick fix from the docs
to kill the pain. (Last time
it took twenty minutes to find a vein
in some poor fucker's arm.)

I'm grinning for you now
through the plate-glass window.
Dummies. Wearing matching faces
which you laid out on the bed last night
to see if they went OK

with the white shirt and black tie.
You've starched your morals stiff,
tucked them tight as napkins
in your high-and-mighty collars.
'For what you are about to receive.'
All you can eat for thirty dollars.
I hope you had the good grace
to wash your hands before you came.

Miniature Rose

It's an impulse buy. Affordable.
Her weekly treat.
She likes the petite petals
and tiny thorns
soft as a baby's nails.

Sheathed in cellophane,
it shivers on the back seat of the car.
At home it's left on the sill
above the storage heater.
Pot-bound. Scentless.

At night, leaves pressed
against the cold pane,
the moon like an empty saucer,
it might be dreaming —
one last, grand gesture:

martyred between the white teeth
of a Spanish dancer,
or skidding recklessly across the ice
towards the bladed feet of a skater.
Glorious applause. A row of sixes.

She forgets to water it —
the odd dribble
from a cloudy milk bottle.
The leaves turn brown
and drop. The soil dessicates.

Each morning she waits for the kettle
to boil, picks coffee granules
from the sugar bowl.
Each night she wipes
the *Things To Do* board clean.

One day, its deadness will surprise her.
She will crumble leaves
like dried herbs between her fingers,
their stale dust
flavouring the air.

By Heart

You wash the glasses first — your best —
cut, lead crystal in my honour.
You handle them with rubber gloves,
careful as a nurse, sponging away
the dregs of wine, the smudged edges
where lips have touched.

'. . . so why *doesn't* it rhyme?
When I was your age
I had bits of Hardy off by heart.'
Smiling, I respond:
I leant upon a coppice gate
when frost was spectre grey . . .
Your voice joins mine,
faltering at first, then stronger,
recovering the lost cadence:

two girls in the same town
and thirty years apart
are swinging in time
up and down, higher and higher,
till letting go,
they hang weightless
for a second in the air,

landing perfectly, together:
Some blessed Hope, whereof he knew
and I was unaware.
You lift the last glass,
sparkling, from the water.

I stoop to kiss you,
putting my arms
around your curving spine.
'Goodnight.' 'Goodnight.'
You go on ahead,
leaving me behind
to lock up
and turn out the lights.

Miserere

You are lining up your normal pills —
a small white one with a long name,
a slick capsule of pink and black.
Your pulse slows. Rain.
Dusk slurring into night.
By nine, you're dead to the world.

In another life, you took me
to hear Allegri's masterpiece.
We huddled in the stone cold, awed
as the highest note a choirboy can reach
soared free of the bars of manuscript
and hung in the twilight of the church.

Jolted awake. 3 a.m. The rain still lashing.
You've left my side,
stumbled in the darkness
down the stairs. I find you,
naked and bleeding, moaning *fuck it*
in a broken voice.

Ten Poems

HELEN OSWALD

Helen Oswald was born in Tunisia in 1965. After graduating from London University she worked in journalism and publishing. She currently lives in south-east London.

Sting

Apples are as good a place to start as any;
apples and four wet wellingtons glistening like slugs
in the bladed grass. Me and my brother. My mother is in brogues
that darken as we pick up windfalls, soaked and squeaking,
and drop them in an aluminium tub.

We carry them to the top floor and are shown how to space them
gently in rows on the pages of yesterday's *Daily Telegraph,*
taking care not to bruise them. We are sick to death
of a thousand apple-themed desserts and secretly bump them
while our mother kneels by the skirting board.

A few months later, sent up to weed out the rotten ones,
we work amidst the cidery stink, filling seed boxes
and lugging them down three flights. Finally we hit on the idea
of opening the bolted fire-escape and flinging them
one hundred feet into the hen-run below.

And run they do. Their wings fan out, flaring
like plane crashes on a radar screen. We dash back and forth
for more ammo, thrilled, until I grab a good one,
a hard one. Then we notice one hen has not moved for ages.
This is our first death.

★

That was the spring before the bee funerals.
I lifted the dead ones
by dried Sellotape wings
and laid each in a separate tulip.
They closed as night fell.
I dreamt of lying on a pollen bed,
waiting for the light to bleed
through silk red petals
and for the sky to open.

Sunday School Party

Our father blew fishes down the endless village hall.
Buttocks jutting like a mule, he scuttled amidst
his origami shoal. We watched appalled.
After fifty Sundays, robed and revered,
up in his crow's nest, pointing towards land,
how could he stoop to this?

— *Oh God, let it be over.*
— *No.*

One fish, in a salty, curling betrayal,
turned and slid under a trestle table. Our father,
propelling himself in great knuckled thrusts,
was after it. The table held and then collapsed,
as it was designed to.

The Magic Hour

We waited for the magic hour,
lying in long grass until
the sun would slide like honey down the lens,
you turning your kaleidoscope to make
the sky fall into place.

Dry July days stretched out
taut as mousetraps, one eye
on the letter-box for brown envelopes,
grades bunched like fists
at the beginning of the alphabet.

Punk was in. We pored over buckets,
tie-dyeing T-shirts, bleaching jeans,
the house all door-slam and vinyl clangour;
dinner a reverb of parental pleading,
nights holding our fire.

The picture developed. Nobody knows
I keep fields and the sun
shut up in a drawer. I open it most evenings
and blink at that yellow second
you stole from the universe.

Full Tilt

We seemed to spend our lives falling off bikes.
Come back home now in cars, we yearn for the heroics
of bony saddles, of braving it without brakes, lights —
'with only the sole of your shoe
and the mercy of God between you and disaster.'

Remember the time I went full tilt down Jab's Hill
on the racer, must have been one-in-four,
the brakes jammed — not a hope in hell.
Cut clean across the Colchester road
like scissors through a ribbon.

And what about the night you switched off your lights
flying back from music practice, to enjoy the moon,
as though it was a dynamo, forgetting the clouds.
The violin only saved
by being already in its coffin.

Or the time we cycled two-abreast. No hands.
The handlebars locked horns and joined us at the hip.
One moment of perfect fusion,
until we came apart, you and I
like a book falling open.

The New Pitch

Hungry for new ground, heart-sore for the old,
the Millwall fans crash in, fresh from The Den —
tight with disallowed tears, stolen turf, goals
fit to burst; the last match lost — Englishmen.
Ill-advised bar staff deny them and duck.
They pick up and pitch ashtrays full-square
into mirrors, wreck The Mayflower — 'Fuck
you, bastards!' Fast arms flash, reflections tear,
the air cracks and rings, rains glass, shards sparkle
like smash-and-grab diamonds. Pints jostle, spill,
hit the deck and break into wet petals.
Time slows right down and stops. We watch them, thrilled,
as silence falls; dumb with fascination,
while sirens hail their brilliant destruction.

Africa meets Hockney at The Royal Academy

A forest chopped and boxed, shipped
abroad, spotlit and plaqued.

Next door, Hockney's crayon draws
Bradford, prophesies a blue rapport.

Jagged quartz a million years old prefigures
a world crystallized, of prisms.

New York '75. Robert transubstantiates in pink,
Gregory, angel-eyed, appears in the wings.

Objects hold sway over human purpose:
God is wood; the artist is nameless.

By '82 Gregory becomes a man. Celia despairs,
lies couched in a scribble of hair.

The female deity rocks, life-size, bored
on her plinth. Seen it all before.

Hockney's mother has grown old. Stanley, pup,
curls in a ring, keeps one lid up.

Down in the tube we shut eyes, watch it flash past:
memory is Cubist.

Patience

You know exactly the name
of every bone in my anatomy
and point out, gently, my
supraclavicular fossa.

You lower your head expertly
onto the shipwreck of my ribs,
explaining that although my heartbeat
is irregular, there is no danger.

Tender exploration tells you
by what tool and what technique
the obstetrician cut me from my mother
that torpid morning in Tunisia.

I listen patiently, dying to defy
your dictionary. At last
when we are wordless, I run my hand
across the simple language of your body.

Home Entertainment

No, let's stay home, let me be your circus:
along our ceiling I'll string a trapeze, dangle
upside-down in Lycra by my toes, bring on
two tigers to crouch by your feet, see their teeth
bare. I will wear a dinner-jacket to tame them,
saliva will sparkle, silver on the sleeves, danger
shine in an eye. I will walk on my hands
through mid-air, cartwheel up walls, juggle
six lit candles. You will applaud, of course.

Before you can get bored, I will fold
pages of the Sunday paper into falcons,
perch them on picture rails. That carpet
is wasted on the floor; I'll get it airborne, sit
cross-legged in my turban. Climb up! Let's visit
the kitchen, shrink in a hot wash, go sailing in the sink.
The freezer is ripe for polar exploration: we'll play
ice hockey with peas, ride on the backs of cod.

Through with showbiz we will retire,
punch flat our black top hats, shake off our tails.
We'll unpack pillows, spread a nest of curled, white feathers,
breast-stroke them to the four corners. Take down curtains,
hang them at our heads and feet, right and left —
a four-poster fit for Henry VIII and half a dozen wives. Yes,
in one evening at home, we'll have the time of our lives.

Poles Apart

I hold a candle in to thaw ice,
hacking with knives until the fish yield
like Neanderthals from tundra.
My hand exhales. Mist-wrapped,
it breaks a ship's passage through icebergs.
Meals we meant to eat together
come to room temperature.

Cuts

Evening starts its engine in our vacuumed town.
He selects a dress, encircles its waist
and waltzes to the bed, croons — let me be
a woman for a night.

He is made up, beautiful, groomed
right down to the twentieth cuticle —
show me the ghost of your smile,
my reconditioned only child.

In a hobbled street the club girls clatter,
all hooves and hair, teeth and eyes
for the main chance. Smoking nostrils,
bolted hearts — thoroughbreds.

Shy boys hold them to it, fumbled
seductions in single beds. They dread
the big time, but here it is —
their own worst enemy at last.

★

Under the blue skin of the Lloyd's building
a lift forms a lump in its five-o'clock throat,
automatic doors decline to open,
offer them up to velvet pubs.

Tonight in the temple of Charing Cross, we watch
departure boards for the word of God, destinations
spelling home; home after the scary day,
so packed with people passing go.

★

He comes in alone and leaves alone,
eyes raking faces for recognition.
Behind the bar the optics gulp it down.

She knows she hasn't long, builds a shaky bridge
into the next world, raises a wobbly glass
to the dubious future.

They are eating eye to eye, fleshy pasta
off bone china, polished feet planted under tables.
Their waiter leans and whistles.

In a burgled house someone stops to mock the cops,
smoke a cigarette, stroll through ransacked rooms,
open their holiday post.

Paper aeroplanes lift off as night
reveals itself, black and blue.
They get home late with a take-away.

★

She gives him a massage.
His body is bagpipes, full
of soft air, fingered bones
squeezing out wheezy tunes.
She tells him, everything

in the world looks and sounds
but does not smell like anything else.
A coffee bean resembles
a rugby ball, rattles like dice,
smells like coffee, and is.

In one minute they visit
the radio stations of a hundred nations,
search in tongues and thread
a phosphorescent needle through
the spine of time —

notes float into the next dimension.
Some day in the past astronomers
will listen, astonished, as a probe
returns the sound of Pulp,
of the Common People.

★

The last leaf drops,
breaks its back coming down,
lands, dead as a stunt man.

Later snow will settle
and shoes will print
the skeletons of fish.

But afternoon holds still,
holds every living thing
nailed to the second-hand planet.

Stomach

SCOTT PERRY

Scott Perry *was born in 1971 and studied English at Durham University. His play* Sketches in the Dark *won the 1994 National Student Playwriting Competition and his play* Bookends *was published by Samuel French in April.*

Characters: Dragon
               Fudge
               Two policemen
               John

DRAGON *is tall,* FUDGE *is short,* JOHN *has a Midlands drawl.*

Two pairs of feet are scuttling around a golf driving range. The smaller pair, FUDGE's, *are in heavy-set boots with a zip and buckle.* DRAGON *wears cheap black work shoes. It is raining. The feet move randomly, haphazardly, drunkenly from ball to ball. They are collecting: they grab the balls, and deposit them in any one of the following places: jacket pockets, jean pockets, socks, underpants. This goes on for some time. Eventually we become aware that the two people are laughing, and the laughter seems to build and build until the booted feet slip and fall. Then silence. The camera is moving up* FUDGE's *prostrate body.*

DRAGON   Fudge? Fudge? You fuckin' idiot. You daft bast'd. Fudge. Wake up.

A foot thuds into FUDGE's *midriff.* FUDGE *opens one eye.* FUDGE's *point of view:* DRAGON *leaning over him. The laughter begins again.*

Cut to:
They are staggering back across the field, heading for the fence.

DRAGON What a laugh. What a laugh, eh? What a laugh, dontcha reckon? Fudge. Eh, Fudge?

FUDGE *has begun to veer left.*

DRAGON Fudge. Fudge, this way.

FUDGE *veers back to the right, picking up another ball on the way.*

Cut to:
The other side of the fence. A police car is parked where they are climbing over. They are making a horrible job of it. The OFFICERS are watching with blank faces, the nearside window wound down. The nearside OFFICER gives the mildest of winces and looks at his watch.

DRAGON *and* FUDGE *are oblivious to the car. Finally they climb over, stand up. Brush themselves down. See the car.* FUDGE *heads straight for the back door and gets in.*

FUDGE Eighteen Dean Street.

OFFICER Get out the car, pal.

FUDGE Get out the car. Dean Street, please.

OFFICER Get out of the car.

FUDGE'*s drunkenness heeds the* OFFICER'*s tone, and after a half-second pause, he does so, automatically, like a robot.* DRAGON *gives the policemen a self-conscious little wave.*

OFFICER Would you like to explain why you were climbing that fence?

They stand on the pavement, like schoolboys, staring inanely back.

FUDGE We climbed it because it was there.

This hangs in the air.

DRAGON *(hurriedly)* No, no, no, we climbed it because we thought it was a short cut, we thought we'd try a short cut, but no, it went wrong, so we climbed back again. Isn't that right, Fudge?

FUDGE *(great certainty)* No.

> *The rain comes down.*
> *The* OFFICERS *stare.*
> *A golf ball falls from* DRAGON*'s pocket and bounces on the concrete pavement. Once, then twice, then several times, progressively faster. The ball rolls to a halt in the gutter.*
> *The rain comes down.*

OFFICER Any idea where that may have come from?

> DRAGON *blows out in mock innocence.*
> FUDGE *copies him.*
> *The* OFFICER *holds out a carrier bag. They fill the carrier bag with the balls. They empty their jacket pockets. Pause. It is clear the* OFFICER *wants more. They empty their inside jacket pockets. Then stop again.*

OFFICER And the rest.

> *They empty their jeans pockets. Then stop again.*

FUDGE And the rest.

> DRAGON *seems a little put out by this. He finds more balls in his socks.*

OFFICER That'll do.

DRAGON Hold on.

He produces more.

OFFICER That's fine, thank you.

DRAGON puts another in the carrier bag as the OFFICER hauls it back in through the window. Then a curt nod.
DRAGON fishes out another ball. The OFFICER stares, then holds his hand out and takes it.

OFFICER Know what your problem is? No balls.

The two OFFICERS break out into laughter. DRAGON tries his best to laugh along, trying to be party to the joke. FUDGE laughs loudly, but late.
The car pulls off.
Ten yards down the road the policeman's hand emerges from the window and waves.
Tentatively DRAGON lifts a hand in response.
DRAGON and FUDGE shuffle off, past the ball which fell first from DRAGON's pocket: this occupies the foreground of the shot.

Cut to:
DRAGON and FUDGE urinating behind a wall. The height of the wall highlights their difference in size: whereas we can see most of DRAGON's torso, it cuts FUDGE off at the neck.

DRAGON They were all right, weren't they. They were all right. That was one of those moments, wasn't it, wasn't it, Fudge, makes you feel good, makes you feel right. One of those moments.

Sound of footsteps. A slow, rather podgy youth, JOHN, is shuffling home.
DRAGON and FUDGE, full of drunken bonhomie, cheer and wave: DRAGON first.
JOHN shuffles on, one furtive look round, but he ignores them and quickens his step.
DRAGON pulls a perplexed frown. He turns to FUDGE.

DRAGON I don't think we're that scary, do you?

FUDGE What?

DRAGON It's just bloody manners, isn't it?

Zipping himself up, DRAGON *marches off round the corner after* JOHN. JOHN *is already running.* DRAGON *sees this and gives chase, quickly followed by* FUDGE. *The frame freezes.*

DRAGON *(over still)* What's he running for? Tell me why he's running. I'm not a criminal, I'm not a thug.

The action continues. From behind we see JOHN *struggling. He is clearly extremely unfit, and the pair, despite their drunkenness, are easily gaining on him.*
We see him go down. Particular attention to the sound he makes as he falls against the concrete in real time. The picture freezes.

DRAGON *(over still)* Jesus, that's ugly.

Close-up on JOHN. *From before he fell: we view the fall again in slow motion.*

DRAGON *(over slow motion)* I never, ever, want to see this again, his legs giving way, Jesus. I never asked to see it and I never want to see it again.

The fall is complete. The action continues at normal speed. JOHN *is panting, heaving, dribbling: horrendously vulnerable; beached like a whale. The footsteps rapidly approach: they seem menacing and fearsome.* JOHN *seems unable to get up.*
They arrive like a pair of Labradors; their concern is genuine.

DRAGON Are you all right, mate?

FUDGE Are you OK?

JOHN What?

DRAGON I'm so sorry. Really we are.

FUDGE We didn't want you to fall.

DRAGON We don't mean any harm. At all.

FUDGE We're just sorry.

DRAGON We're sorry. We're so, so sorry.

FUDGE Are you all right?

DRAGON Honestly, we're really sorry.

FUDGE Yeah.

DRAGON We were just waving at you.

FUDGE Can you get up? Are you all right?

JOHN What?

DRAGON We're not going to harm you.

FUDGE We're completely decent people.

DRAGON That's why we're apologising.

FUDGE Yeah.

DRAGON That's why we chased you.

FUDGE Here, have ten pounds.

DRAGON Honestly, really sorry. We never meant that to happen.

FUDGE Here, let me give you a hand up.

DRAGON Honestly.

FUDGE Come on.

DRAGON You just didn't wave back.

FUDGE Brush you down. Are you hurt?

DRAGON Why didn't you wave?

JOHN Jesus. I thought I was a gonner then.

DRAGON I bet you did. You should have waved.

JOHN Sorry.

DRAGON No. We're sorry. We're really sorry.

FUDGE Sorry.

JOHN Looks like I'm still in one piece.

DRAGON I'm Dragon.

FUDGE I'm Fudge.

JOHN (*wary*) I'm John.

   Pause.

DRAGON Mmm.

FUDGE Not very exciting, is it?

DRAGON Not very interesting.

JOHN It's not really, is it.

DRAGON No, it isn't. Rocket. We'll call you Rocket.

FUDGE Rocket.

JOHN Rocket.

DRAGON You know we're really sorry about what happened back there. I mean in some ways it was probably worse for us than you. It was horrible to watch. You know, and here we are talking, considering that two minutes ago you thought you were going to be . . . you know, so . . . why not come for a drink. That's the thing. We feel terrible. Please. It's the least we can do.

Pause. JOHN eyes them.

JOHN I'm game for anything, me.

Cut to:
A fridge. Packed with cans of Kestrel; one can of Theakston's XB. The door opens. Pause. A hand reaches in, dithers: freeze.

DRAGON *(over freeze)* Maybe I'm over-sensitive. Maybe I am. But look. Not your fridge. You're offered a beer. Look. Look. Would you? Would you? I wouldn't.

The hand grabs the can of Theakston's.

Cut to:
A very small sitting room. There is one large armchair, dark green, with large flat arms. There is a small table. There is a large picture of a block of flats being demolished, one of those that shows the building at the point of toppling to earth. This is the only picture. There is one cut-out of a soccer player shooting stuck to the wall: this from a newspaper. There is also a pink two-seater sofa, which is quite hard, small and upright: uncomfortable. The sound of a toilet flushing. FUDGE has sat on the pink sofa. JOHN is in the

armchair, drinking the Theakston's. He sits with his legs apart.

DRAGON *(entering the room)* Oh.

JOHN *(following a long swig)* That's all right, isn't it?

DRAGON You, er, you thought you'd, er . . . fine. Fine. No, don't worry about it.

JOHN *isn't. He puts the beer down, claps his hands and rubs them together.*

JOHN Right. Here we are then.

FUDGE *shuffles out.*

DRAGON *(trying to remain sincere)* You thought you'd have the Theakston's, did you? No, that's OK, that's OK. I hope you enjoy it.

JOHN Nice gaff.

DRAGON *(looking at the can)* I won it.

JOHN No you never. Very nice, though.

DRAGON The beer, I won the beer.

JOHN Oh right.

DRAGON So please appreciate it. That's all I ask.

JOHN Theakston's, yeah.

DRAGON Yeah.

JOHN Not bad, not bad. Not the best, but not bad.

DRAGON *(pointed)* Better than Kestrel.

FUDGE arrives with two cans of Kestrel, gives one to DRAGON, and sits down. His movements are quite robotic, as if the drinking impulse is on autopilot. He opens the can, sips.

JOHN He doesn't say much, does he? Your mate.

FUDGE and DRAGON stare blankly at JOHN for a few moments. JOHN goes to the sidelight and turns it on, then pushes past DRAGON and turns the main light off.

JOHN Atmosphere.

DRAGON tries not to look put out. JOHN plonks himself down on the armchair again.

DRAGON Yeah, Rocket, that's my armchair.

JOHN Oh right, sorry.

He gets up. They stand.

DRAGON No, no, forget it, you have it.

JOHN I don't mind. Never fussy, me.

DRAGON Well —

JOHN I don't mind.

DRAGON This is silly.

JOHN Whatever you want, mate.

DRAGON No, no, you er . . . my treat.

DRAGON sits with FUDGE on the sofa. He never looks

quite at home there.

DRAGON So, Rocket, what do you do?

JOHN What do I do? There's only one thing to do, these days, isn't there, only one thing to do. Eh?

DRAGON *and* FUDGE *don't seem to know.*

JOHN Computers. It's the only thing, I.T., it's where — I mean, you *do know* about computers?

DRAGON *gives a tentative nod: he very clearly doesn't.*

JOHN I mean what's going on at the moment is frightening. I mean I'm there, I know about it, but it's moving so fast it's scaring the shit out of me: I'm telling you — what they are capable of now: frightening — I'm telling you: frightening. You know on the outside: so-so, people say it's dull: let them. 'Cause I'll tell you a secret: computers is the biggest buzz. *The* biggest. Bar none. Frightening.

Pause.

DRAGON *(misplaced goodwill)* Right.

JOHN You know what your calling is. You know what you're good at. You get on and do it. I'm not ashamed of that, not by a long chalk.

Cut to:
JOHN *in the bathroom. His speech continues in voice-over. He looks at himself in the mirror. He looks around the room. He breathes in. He breathes out. He looks in the mirror again. He flushes the toilet: the lid is down. He picks up aftershave, looks at it, then puts it in his pocket. He sees an electric razor and pockets that too.*

JOHN *(voice-over)* It fuels me. And I'll tell you this: the thing is, right, and this is unbelievable when you think about it, but it's tantamount to the pace of change: would you believe it if I actually said to you there is a shortage of information technology skilled labour in this country at this time? No, you wouldn't. But there is. And the thing is that if you can keep yourself ahead . . . big money. Big, big money. Oh yes. I mean you think about it. You write a program that performs a function two seconds quicker than any other program. That's what it's all about. Industry buys seconds, it buys all the seconds you can sell it: pays through the nose — you'll sell that program. You'll sell yourself. Seconds count. Believe me. They count all right. They count like you'd never believe.

Cut to:
Pause. JOHN *sits back in his chair, chin into his neck, eyeballs glaring ferociously through his eyebrows; in his element. A lawyer who has just revealed crucial evidence. He puts his feet up.* DRAGON *notices, says nothing, takes his own feet down off the furniture.*

DRAGON *(pointing to the wall)* You see that there. Bobby Charlton. Reckon that was the hardest shot ever hit, that one. That one there.

JOHN How can they possibly tell?

Pause.

DRAGON Do you like football?

JOHN *(he is picking his nose)* I can't say I do. No.

DRAGON Oh.

During this next speech JOHN *very unobtrusively drops his hand to his side and rubs his thumb and forefinger together.*

JOHN I buy seconds for mankind. I buy them, and I sell them on. It's as simple and as far-reaching as that. Boundaries, Dragon, frontiers: I mean you don't say "can't do" these days, you wouldn't dare, 'cause someone is gonna turn around and say "can do." You've got to see that that person is you. You've got to, it's as simple as that. Make it you. You see it was the same at school, right, my parents, my dad in particular, wanted me to become a chemical engineer. Was I having any of it? Was I?

DRAGON *looks on blankly.* FUDGE *appears to have dropped off.*

JOHN Was I hell.

Another dramatic pause.

JOHN No way. No way. I knew what I wanted, I knew what I was interested in. I knew what I was good at.

DRAGON *(clearly bored)* Of course. Yeah.

JOHN *(knowing look. Slavering with ambition)* Yeah. You know my headteacher took them aside, you know, my parents, and said: this boy wants only one thing. He said, you try dragging him away from that computer and it'll be a big mistake. You've got to give him his head.

DRAGON Did he now . . .

JOHN *(missing the joke entirely)* Oh yeah. Well they had to, Drag, they had to. I was writing my own programs at twelve.

The camera freezes on JOHN.

DRAGON *(over still)* Midlands drawl, it's not the prettiest, now is it? Look at him. Bulging eyeballs in a podgy, blotchy face with tousled, matted, mousy hair. Obscene, really. Well he ran, didn't he, ran, didn't wave, he created it, his fault.

Cut to:
FUDGE *asleep on the chair.* DRAGON's *face is close. He has*

FUDGE's *head in his hands.*

DRAGON Fudge. Fudge, you bloody idiot. Wake up, you daft git.

He kicks FUDGE *on the shins.* FUDGE *opens an eye, and, on autopilot, immediately reaches for the beer can, from which he tries to take a swig. There are now several more cans littering the table.* DRAGON's *face is too close to allow this swig to take place.*

FUDGE Excuse me.

DRAGON *is looking at* FUDGE *through narrowed eyes.*

DRAGON You crafty bugger.

FUDGE *forces the beer can between them and sips.* DRAGON *moves away.*

FUDGE Where is he? What time is it?

DRAGON You crafty bugger.

FUDGE Eh?

DRAGON He's nicked some stuff.

FUDGE What?

DRAGON It's missing, I've checked. Missing from the bathroom.

FUDGE Tosser.

DRAGON Well. Well. Maybe. Maybe.

We hear the toilet flush again. JOHN *comes back into the room.*

JOHN Come to think of it, Dragon's quite a strange name. I mean, what's going on there? Why Dragon, you don't even smoke. Do you.

Mind you, that's a filthy habit, all respect to your friend here.

DRAGON *is visibly struggling for something to say.*

JOHN You know, I think, when all's said and done, I quite like John. Really. I think I'd rather John than Rocket. Rocket's not really me, you know, not really. No, call me John if you would.

DRAGON Look, er, John, time is ticking by.

JOHN I'm boring, I know that.

DRAGON No, no, I never said you were boring —

JOHN Won't be the first time I've heard it, but that's OK, take it on the chin, that's me, live to fight another day.

DRAGON No, but I didn't —

JOHN That's OK, mate, that's OK.

DRAGON I did not say that.

JOHN I read between the lines, mate. People. It's OK.

DRAGON It is six o'clock in the morning.

JOHN I've got the hint. Fret no more.

They are walking through to the front door. They stop in the little hallway.

DRAGON Hope you've, er, changed your opinion. You know. A little. After earlier.

JOHN Oh I expect so.

DRAGON Because I'm not worried about boredom. I just don't like a thief.

JOHN I beg your pardon?

DRAGON What's that in your pocket there, Rocket? What are you hiding from me?

JOHN Nothing.

DRAGON Let's see.

JOHN Nothing.

DRAGON You're hiding something.

JOHN No I'm not, no I'm not.

DRAGON Show me.

Pause.

JOHN Search me.

DRAGON I know what you've got.

JOHN *(cocky, he seems to be relishing the confrontation)* Search me, then.

Pause. DRAGON steps forward and goes through JOHN's pockets. There is nothing there. DRAGON steps back, perplexed. As he does so JOHN leans forward and reaches behind DRAGON's ear, producing a golf ball like a magician. There is adrenalin involved in this movement, a kind of unpleasant competitiveness.

JOHN *(pumped up)* What's this, then? What have we got here?

DRAGON *(very confused now)* What do you mean, what's that?

JOHN Well, Dragon?

DRAGON What are you doing, where did you get that?

JOHN Magic.

DRAGON Bollocks, that's mine. Give it back.

JOHN Oh no.

DRAGON That's my ball.

JOHN It's not.

DRAGON Where d'you get it, give it here.

JOHN Oh no, I don't think so. It's mine.

Suddenly DRAGON *throws a punch low into* JOHN's *stomach. The camera freezes on impact.*

DRAGON I hit him, hard under the rib cage. I hit him again and again, until he puffed and gurgled, then threw him out and closed the door behind me.

Cut to:
DRAGON *leans inside the door, slightly out of breath. He is rolling the golf ball around in his fingers. He looks on the verge of tears, quite panicky. Suddenly he screams:*

DRAGON FUDGE!!

Freeze.
Music. Fade out.

Extract from
Last Chance Texaco

CHRISTINE POUNTNEY

Christine Pountney, *born in 1971, is from Montreal. She now lives in London with her husband Richard Skinner, and is currently working on a novel titled* Last Chance Texaco. *This piece is an excerpt from the first section.*

One day my mother let a bum into the house. He rang the doorbell and asked for money. My mother took pity on him and let him in. She gave him a bowl of her home-made soup and thick slices of fresh bread still steaming with little square pads of butter melting in the center. When he had finished, she let him have a shower, lent him my dad's bathrobe and even gave him a shirt and a pair of trousers that my dad never wore anymore. When the man emerged from the bathroom, he looked completely different. I was eight years old, but even I could tell he was very handsome.

He was an Indian from the reservation, just outside of Bella Coola on the coast of British Columbia. He was tall and muscular. He had a noble face and a strong nose like an arrowhead. His skin was flawless. His hair was like ink pouring down his back. When he came back into the kitchen, he sat down again and my mother placed a cup of coffee in his hand. She sat across from him and took one of his cigarettes. I sat at the end of the table with my chin resting in the small bowl of my fists.

He stayed all afternoon and told stories that made my mother laugh. She poured him cup after cup of coffee. The ashtray gradually filled up. She got up and emptied it into the garbage can. I left and went to play in my room. When it started to get dark, I returned to the kitchen. My mother was leaning across the table and had her hand on his. She was saying something soothing like she was consoling him. When she saw me come in, she gave his hand a quick squeeze then got up and started busying herself at the counter. She made a couple of sandwiches. She put a few bottles of beer into a plastic bag, some fruit and the sandwiches. Then she left the room.

I looked up at the Indian. He stared back at me from his chair. He raised one arm and reached behind his back. He drew an invisible arrow from a quiver and slotted the groove into the string of his bow. He pulled the string back as far as it would go, straining the wood. He released his fingers and let the arrow fly. It hit me full in the chest. I felt the thunk of metal and stumbled backwards. He laughed. He got out of his chair and walked over to me and tousled my hair. He lifted me up and swung me around the room.

Little fella soars like a bird, he laughed, as I careened through the air.

My mother came back into the kitchen and the Indian put me down. She walked over to the counter and slipped an envelope into the plastic bag. She handed him the bag and said, You'd better hurry up. He followed her to the door.

Two weeks later, my mother ran away. I never saw her again. I came home from school to an empty house. The lights were on and there was a bowl of cold soup on the table and a peanut-butter sandwich. On the top slice lay the torn-off corner of a page of loose-leaf. She had drawn a heart in black pen and coloured it in with red Magic Marker. I put the heart inside my sandwich face down on the peanut butter and squeezed it shut. I ate the soup first and then polished off the sandwich. I even ate my crusts.

After my mom left, my dad started drinking a lot and getting into fights. He'd come home in the middle of the night. His face started to change. His eyes lost their sheen, like pebbles on the beach that are brilliant underwater but go grey and mat when you bring them home. His mouth grew tight and wiry like a coil or a spring, ready to shoot off at any minute. He lost his job at the cannery. He was forced to borrow money.

He spent a lot of the time in front of the TV. He'd sit on the sofa with a bottle of beer in one hand and a cigarette in the other. His face was expressionless. He looked exhausted. I'd watch the ash of his cigarette burn down to the filter. He never cooked. I made myself toast. I ate tuna straight out of the can.

One night as I lay awake in my bed there was a loud banging at the door. I heard men's voices and the door slam. A man said, OK,

Orin. It's time to pay up.

I have a son to think about, my dad pleaded in a voice I hardly recognized.

There was a scuffle and a chair fell backwards. I heard a few muffled thuds and a whimper. Something exploded like a fuse-box and glass shattering. I slid off my bed and crept underneath. I listened to my own breathing. I stared at the crack of light under my door. The men left. I pulled my knees up to my chest.

I didn't move until the morning when all the shadows in my room were gone and daylight had made it safe. I tried to stand but my legs were cramped with cold. I rubbed my thighs and stretched out on the floor. When I felt strong enough, I went out to the hall and walked into the living room. My dad lay curled up on his side by the TV. The whole screen was smashed. I looked down at my dad. There was a lump like a dough-ball where his eye should have been.

Are you OK? I asked.

He groaned.

Should I call an ambulance?

He rolled on to his back and grabbed my ankle. He held it very tight for a couple of minutes. When he released it, I went into the kitchen and poured myself a glass of water. I made my dad a cup of coffee. I put a cigarette in his mouth and lit a match. My hands were steady but my heart trembled.

We left that afternoon. My dad put all our clothes into three big garbage bags and threw them into the back seat. He packed two pillows and our sleeping bags, some records and his shaving kit. He took a photo album from his dresser. I walked into my room and pulled a blank. I wanted to take everything but my dad had told me, Only take what you can't replace.

I left my felt pens and my colouring books. I left my teddy bear. I left my rock collection and my plastic tomahawk with the fake feathers. As I was leaving my room, I unhooked my mask and snorkel from the doorknob and put them on. We backed out of the drive and I watched the house recede in the oval frame of my mask. I turned around and hung my arms over the back of the front seat. I watched as my street disappeared behind the fogged-up glass of my deep-sea diving mask. I listened to the rise and fall of my own hot breath. Drool collected in the bend of my snorkel. We drove south out of Bella Coola for the very last time.

After an hour, we stopped at a drive-in and ate hamburgers and fries. I spilt ketchup on the seat and looked up at my dad expecting to be told off. He looked indifferently at the ketchup smudge on the brown upholstery, then continued to stare out the front windshield. He took another bite of his hamburger and winced. Maybe it was the pain in his jaw that was preoccupying him, but he didn't say anything for the whole next leg of the journey. We kept heading south until we hit the American border. We slowed down and glided up to the border station. My dad turned to me and said, Take that thing off. I peeled off my mask and pulled the warm, wet snorkel out of my mouth. It smelt like grease and ketchup. My dad leaned out the window and exchanged a few words with the man in the booth.

Fishing trip, my dad answered. It's a holiday.

Looks like you need one, the border guard said. Hope they're biting, he called and waved us on.

Five miles down the road, my dad pulled over on the side of the highway. He reached across me and pulled his passport out of the glove compartment. He leaned back in his seat and flipped through the blank pages. Then he tore it up. He wound his window down and watched the little shreds of paper float to the ground.

We're starting over, he said then spun the tires on the gravel and took off. It was spring and the wind blew in cool. I tucked my scarf into my collar and hunkered down for the long haul. I had no idea where we were headed. I don't think my dad did either. I looked back down the highway. In the wake of a semi, I saw the small, white petals of my dad's passport rise and scatter across the road.

Two months later we settled down in a little shack surrounded by pines on the edge of a small town called Round Bay, on the coast of California. My dad committed welfare fraud and we lived off his meagre allowance. He enrolled me in the local school and lied about our papers. Life ran a pretty straight course until the summer I was fifteen.

★

You're going to kill yourself one day, my father said when he saw me standing in the kitchen with a towel slung over my shoulder.

Naw. Not in the water, I said. You might, but I'd never. I can't drown . . . I'm a fish, I added, taking the milk from the fridge and drinking straight out of the carton.

You're crazy is what you are.

No, I'm not.

Just don't expect any sympathy from me when you break your neck.

I won't, I said standing in the cool light of the fridge watching the steam roll out like spirits around my feet.

And get me a beer seeing as you've been staring into the fridge for the last twenty minutes.

Get it yourself.

Don't give me any lip, John.

So don't call me crazy, I mumbled placing a King Can on the arm of the living-room sofa.

I'll call you what I like. Now beat it.

I am, I said and walked over to the door and shoved my feet into my sneakers.

I left the house and walked through the pine woods sloping up to the bluffs. I knew the way by heart, which was good because it was very dark. A thin quarter-moon sliced through the upper branches and stars flicked on and off like city lights. The forest creaked with night-time.

When I got to the point, I stripped down to my shorts and stretched my arms over my head then behind my back. I felt the tug and pressure of muscle, then a rush of blood. I walked to the edge of the cliff and looked down at the water. The sea was churning, the waves moving in, then pulling back, carving ancient signatures into the rock. I knew I had to time my dive. If I dove too soon, then I'd be swept up and thrown against the boulders. I had to enter the water just as it was going out, and ride the wave until I was at a safe distance and could swim around the point and back to shore.

My toes curled and gripped the edge like monkey feet. I stared at the black water thirty feet below. I bent my knees and stood poised like a slingshot. I closed my eyes and listened to a wave pound the coast and the after-hiss as it dragged itself out again. Another wave crashed and rumbled like thunder. It dissolved into white froth. I waited for the next one to atomize. I launched myself into the spray. I heard the wind in my ears just before I hit the water. Cold rushed into my armpits. My balls seized up. Everything was soundless and dark. The water pulled me along in somersaults. I felt the bubbles rushing out of my nostrils. I held my breath and waited for the buoyancy of my lungs to draw me up and then I knew which way to go. I kicked my feet and broke the surface of the water, panting for breath.

I got up the next day and rode into town. I propped my bicycle outside Shirley's Diner and walked in. There were six booths on the left side and a long Formica counter on the right with six red vinyl-covered stools. The fourth one was cracked and taped and pinched the skin on the back of my thighs. I only ever sat on that one if all the other ones were taken. The left wall was covered in red and black felt wallpaper, too plush for a dive like this, like something left over from an old frontier brothel, not a saloon. This was not a saloon. Every booth had a beat-up old juke box with about twelve singles apiece, but Shirley didn't like loitering, so she let the singles warp and bend and never bothered replacing them. Sometimes the radio would be on with the baseball game or the golden oldies.

The right wall behind the counter was one big mirror. It had wire-thin, copper-coloured fissures painted on it so that it looked like marble. The first thing I always saw, when I swung the door open Clint Eastwood-style, and the little bell wagged on its hook, was the back of Shirley's head reflected in the mirror. Shirley was overweight and had a bouffant hair-do that she dyed and styled once a week. She was in her fifties and had been running the place ever since my dad and I'd been living in Round Bay. She always wore a blue apron with white trim and her name stitched in cursive across her right breast.

The place was just winding down after the breakfast rush. Shirley took one look at me and clucked her tongue. Sit down, she said and pushed me hard on to a stool and I'm glad to say it wasn't the fourth one because I had on a pair of cut-offs that day.

Your father was in yesterday.

I didn't think he ever left the house.

Yah, well he came round yesterday.

And?

Well, he was trying to sell Mick a bicycle.

Where the fuck's he gonna get a bicycle from?

Watch you mouth, kid.

He doesn't own one.

He wants to trade yours.

He can't have my bike!

Asked Mick if he'd take it in exchange for some credit at the store.

What the fuck's Mick gonna do with my bike?

Mick's got a kid, you know.

Mick's got a girl.

Well, your dad came in here saying you were a lazy bum, did nothing but ride that damn bicycle of yours, and sit on the beach all night like some moron. Asked me if I thought you was queer.

Shirley was leaning on the counter and talking in a redneck accent so that both of us were smiling by the time she'd finished.

Just thought I'd let you know, John. Your dad thinks you're a good-for-nothing sonuvabitch.

Yah, so what's new? I asked and stared a hole into the counter top. How come if you're not cruising chicks or vandalizing the town people think you're lazy or queer round here?

That's just what they're used to. They don't expect you to be any different, John. But you are.

That's not my fault.

I'm not saying it is, she said wiping her hands on her apron. God, that dog out there's been barking all morning.

Whose is it?

I don't know. But I wish someone would put it out of its misery. You hungry? Had any breakfast? How 'bout some waffles?

Shirley went into the kitchen. When she came out, she said to me, What you need is a girl.

What I need is a boat, I replied. I got an idea for a business. Scuba-diving. I could fetch things down there — it's beautiful, Shirley — abalone, coral, starfish. I could take the tourists out. Get the gear. A license.

We don't get any tourists, John. Town's too small.

But we're so close to Santa Barbara. All those resorts? We're not far from LA, either.

Yah, but the folk here ain't much to look at, if you know what I mean.

Halfway through her sentence, someone leaned on a car horn outside and kept blasting it. That horn was going and going, that dog, barking and barking, making a racket and disrupting everybody. Jesus Christ.

Shirley stopped fussing with the glasses she was drying and rolled her eyes at me. We waited but the noise wouldn't stop.

Aw, shut the fuck up! one customer yelled.

People in the diner began to lift themselves out of their chairs to peer into the street. Two old men with hats standing outside the window pointed at something and shook their heads. Shirley slapped her dishtowel down on the counter and nodded to me.

Let's go see what this is all about.

She swung the door open, making the red-and-white checkered curtains swish. I followed her out onto the sidewalk and we headed towards an old, blue Chevy pick-up, where the honking was coming from. It said Foxy's Fresh Seafood Daily in crooked letters across the side. The sun was glaring off the windshield and we had to get pretty close to see into the cab. When we were close enough, we saw that there in the driver's seat sat a dog with its paw up on the horn, like a petulant child, domineering the whole main street in town.

Shirley laughed and smacked the window. The dog bounded to the other side, the honking stopped, and the dog stuck its tongue out the window.

I was just leaving the grocery store with a stolen green apple and a brand new Super Heroes comic book rolled up in my back pocket, when Ben called me from across the street. He jogged over.

Hey, you old shit! Where the fuck you been?

Here.

I mean I've been looking for you since school got out. Where ya been?

Here. The beach.

I been to the beach every afternoon since school got out.

I don't go in the afternoon.

Well, you missed a show. Babe got drunk on Saturday and this time everybody got to see her tits.

Sorry I missed it, I said.

Man, I've been beating off to those tits for years.

Everybody has. What happened?

Well, the guys told her Mr. Brodsky was going to be at the beach, you know, the new English teacher every girl is gaga over? So she came down in a bikini. Can you believe it? Holy fuck! You should've seen her. Out to here! Nothing holding her back. So we kept giving her beer and after she'd had almost a whole six pack, Derrick goes up to her from behind and unclips her bikini top and runs off with it. She was too drunk to chase him, sort of stumbled after him down the beach. We were just killing ourselves laughing. But I bet you every guy there had a fucken hard-on. Hey! You listening to me, or what?

Yah, yah, I said and looked up towards the sun so that the tops of the telephone poles along the edge of the street disappeared into a blur of light. The light was burning patterns of telephone poles on to my retina, I could tell. I could feel the hollow balls of my eyes heating up. I forced myself to keep staring until my eyes began to water and blink uncontrollably. I squinted and then out of the haze emerged the figure of a girl. Thick-set and strong looking. Black hair cut short around her square face and lips the colour of pomegranate seeds. She was wearing a black halter-top and blue shorts. She walked right up to me and past me, looked at me quickly and said, Hi. I immediately got this mentholated feeling in my chest, like when you rub Vick's Vapour Rub on it then breathe in vigorously.

Ben swivelled on his heels and let out a whistle. She's the new girl, he said. Just moved here with her father. She's foreign. Got a weird last name.

What's her name? I asked still staring in the direction she had come from.

Dunno. Hey! Snap out of it. You look like you've just seen a ghost.

Ben shoved me, then punched me square in the shoulder which made me close my mouth.

Aw, forget it, he said. You're fucken hopeless.

I spent all afternoon thinking about the new girl. I needed some way to impress her. She was beautiful and I had nothing. I decided to go see Peter. Peter was a fisherman and had a plywood boat-house on the beach.

Hey there, John, he said from the other side of a knotted fishing-net that he was checking for tears. Haven't seen you in a while.

I been around.

I know you have. Just haven't seen you, that's all.

How's the fishing?

Not too bad.

Got any work?

What kind of work?

Any kind.

You need some cash, John?

I want to buy a boat.

A boat, huh?

Yep.

What kind of boat? A schooner? Hauler? Rig? Just what kind of a boat are you aiming to buy there, Johnny boy?

I know a bit about boats. I'm not claiming to be an expert, but I'm not as naive as all that. I understand the water.

You understand the water, huh? So tell me, how much have you learned in all your years?

I know its power 'cause I've felt it. I respect the ocean. It needs honouring.

Honouring? I'm sure it'd be pleased to hear that. But honour's a bit lofty a sentiment, don't you think? You can't just go out on the water without having any technique. What if something happened? What if you capsized? What if there was an emergency? Do you know the signal for danger? For help? You have to know about tides and currents, weather systems and coastal lights. You wanna make sure other boats can see you. You have to learn to navigate and read maps. What if you got caught in a squall? There are offshore drifts that'd carry you to Mexico before you had the chance to say Jack Daniels, and then what?

There was an awkward pause. I shuffled the sand between my toes. Peter looked embarrassed and fidgeted with the net.

A row-boat, I said quietly. Just a fucken row-boat . . .

I got a row-boat out back needs scraping and a paint job. It'll take you a while to do it but in return you can have Lil, the one that's upturned. Still needs a lot of work, but you can have her today if you start on the other one this week, how's that?

I smiled and shook Peter's hand. Thanks man, and something slow and lifeless in me slid off like a snake's skin, and something hopeful and energetic remained in its place. I ran back behind the shed and righted my boat. Lil. The hull had holes. The bench was rotting in the middle and eaten away by termites. I was overjoyed. I made a mental list of things I had to do.

I had a boat. I had a chance to get the girl.

I was cycling down Main Street the next time I saw her. She was walking into Mick's Green Grocers. I jumped off my bike before bringing it to a stop and charged into the store. The transition into darkness blinded me and I nearly bumped into her at the counter.

Hi, Mick. Gimme some razors! And four of those Jaw Breakers! I cried almost hysterically, fumbling in my pocket for some change.

Three sixty-five, John. What's the matter with you today?

Three? I whined fishing around in my other pocket. Um . . .

Want me to put it on your dad's tab?

No! Just forget the razors. Here's a buck for the Jaw Breakers. Aw Christ! I swore as I knocked the small paper bag over and two electric-blue balls rolled across the counter and onto the floor. I didn't bother picking them up. I just ran for the door not daring to look back.

Gotta be puberty, Mick sighed. Helluvan awkward age. Can I help you, Miss?

Out in the naked sunlight, I panicked again because I couldn't see my bike at first. It was lying near the stairs of the shop next door where it had landed unceremoniously. I swung my leg clumsily over the seat, stumbled a few paces, and crushed a testicle between the crossbar and my thigh. Doubled over in pain, I peddled off towards Shirley's.

I limped into the diner and sat down sideways on the edge of a stool and placed my little greasy bag with the two Jaw Breakers on the plate in front of me. The sight of those things nearly made me cry and I was about to tell Shirley to forget my lunch 'cause I had no appetite when the door swung open and the girl walked in. I felt myself go red and quickly swivelled round so that I was facing the mirror and knocked a fork to the floor. Why did Shirley have to set out so much damn cutlery?

Shirley took one look at the girl and said, Wanna milk shake?

Do you have any cake? the girl asked.

No, but we have pie. Apple or cherry. Best in town, isn't that right, John? She turned to me and finished me off with a wink.

Cut it out, Shirley, I thought to myself. I'm dying. I'm absolutely dying here. Help me, for chrissake.

Mind if I sit here? the girl asked.

Mind? I screamed. Hell no! Free world, ain't it! Then sunk back onto my stool and tried as best I could to pull my head inside my shirt collar.

I'll bring you each a piece, Shirley said to the top of my head. Apple or cherry?

I found the question embarrassing. Um . . . apple for me, I mumbled.

Me too, said the girl.

Two apple it is then.

The pie came and we ate it and neither of us said a word. Simultaneously, we both got up to go.

How much do I owe you? the girl asked.

On the house this time, Shirley said with mischief.

As we were leaving, Shirley pulled me aside by the sleeve of my shirt and said, Say something for godssake! And don't be so nervous.

The girl turned to look me square in the face as she pulled the door forward. After you, she said.

Outside we kicked up dust on the sidewalk and I thought this girl must be tough or something. She sticks her hip out way too far when she's just standing around. She's got all these bruises on her body and Band-Aids on both knees. I sat down on the curb to contemplate. The girl also sat down, took a cigarette out of a pack in her pocket, and lit up a smoke.

You shouldn't smoke. It's bad for your lungs.

Aw fuck off, she said.

I can't smoke. I'm not supposed to.

Why, you sick or somethin'?

No.

Then how come?

'Cause I'm a diver. I need all my lung capacity. I can hold my breath up to three, four minutes under water.

Bullshit.

It's true.

No you can't. That's impossible.

I'll show ya.

OK. Right now?

Down at the beach.

OK, she said and brushed her ass off and put the cigarette out with the toe of her sneakers and tucked a stray wisp of hair behind the prettiest little ear, like a rose bud with tiny little leaves and a soft rubbery thorn that hadn't grown brittle yet.

I picked up my bike and we headed for the beach.

So where you from?

Boston.

That's far, isn't it?

Kinda. Not if you fly. It only took us five hours.

What brought you here?

My dad. Wanted a quiet place to work. It's cheap here. And nobody's ever heard of it before. Nobody knows this place even exists. It's like cut off from the outside world.

What does he do?

He's a writer.

And your mom?

How come you ask so many fucken questions?

Sorry . . . ask me one.

How old are you?

I'm seventeen, I said.

Bullshit!

Sixteen.

No, you're not.

I'm fifteen, 'K? I'm fucken fifteen.

Really? Are you really?

Yep. And you?

I'm sixteen. I'll be seventeen in December . . . You're not a very good liar.

She was a whole year older than me. One year older and the most beautiful woman I'd ever laid my sorry eyes on in all my life.

I own a boat, I said. Wanna see it?

Maybe later. I don't know how to swim.

I Am Scrawny, I Am Young, I Will Wear My Jeans Low-Slung

CHARLOTTE PRICE

Charlotte Price grew up in Greenwich Village and has been living and writing in London for the last four years. Her story Piglady *appeared in the 1996 Virago anthology* Short Circuits: Twelve New Writers. *She is currently working on a novel.*

Halfway up the last flight, I stop to feel the wind spiral round the lighthouse and slap me in the face. In the fog, no hard edges. Sea, sky, and shore blur except for the clumps of seaweed that here and there hug the rocks below: charcoal smudges in the light-gray moment before rain.

Behind me, Jordan catches up.

"Move it, Shep." And he shoves me up and out.

We huddle against the wall, pulling the sleeves of our sweaters over our fists. Jordan's are flecked with light-blue paint from jimmying the window open downstairs. He pulls a joint from a half-empty pack of Marlboros and lights it in the cup of his hand, smoke sliding over his tongue and down his throat.

The ring of fringe round the rip in his jeans shudders in the wind.

"Thanks," I mumble, wondering what it would be like to touch that patch of knee.

There'd been a fire, two-and-something months before, and we'd had to evacuate, Mom, my kid sister, Lou, and me — leave the house in the Bluffs and rent a trailer at Paddler's Cove until the insurance money came through and they could start rebuilding. Actually, we spent the first three days in a suite at the Marriott, then went to Paddler's the day after Pingree let out for summer vacation. Mom never said why exactly, but Pingree's a bit on the snotty side. Already we'd had to promise up and down never to let slip how she'd been to court twice to get Dad to pay the tuition; I don't guess she could stand the idea of anyone there knowing she'd ended up on the Paddler's side of the tracks.

That's how I knew Jordan must go to Lincoln, the local public high school, because Lincoln gets out three weeks later than Pingree and the very first morning I happened to wake up just as he was coming out of the trailer diagonally across from ours with a knapsack full of books over his shoulder. After that, I used to wake up early just to watch him, roll over in the sofa bed where I sleep, and lift a corner of the curtain. It's a horrible slick thing, that curtain, nothing you'd necessarily want to touch, but there was this thing he did every morning and I was hooked. It wasn't much, just a way he had of turning back to look at himself in the glass door. Then his hand would go up, like he was going to fix his hair or something, only at the last minute, he swiveled his head, ever so slightly. That was enough to change his mind. The fingers stopped mid-air: he was already perfect. Then, shoulders back, he kind of slid the soles of his high tops down the steps — I used to catch myself counting them — and ambled off to the parking lot like he knew he was being watched. Not that it was down to me or anything, that's just how he walks, like he knows the gods themselves can't help peeking down from behind the clouds. The rest of the day I'd keep my eyes peeled on his trailer but pretty much all I figured out was he lived with two old ladies, a knitter and a bony one, one of whom was bound to be his grandmother.

Meanwhile, Lou wasn't speaking to me, or barely anyway, not since the fire. Partly for the pleasure of seeing Mom's face crumple, or maybe entirely, she got a summer job at the Wash 'n' Dash over at the shopping center, and after that I didn't see a whole lot of her. Still, the silent treatment was beginning to get under my skin. One day I decided to stop by towards the end of her shift to see about walking her home. In our family we don't talk about 'things', talk them out, or talk them over, but sometimes they just go away. If I was hoping this would be one of those times, I took one look at Lou's face and changed my mind.

Lately she'd begun wearing her hair pulled forward over her shoulders. It was her way of coping with what Mom referred to as her 'new figure' — two lank curtains in lieu of a bra — but it gave her a weighed-down, miserable look in the best of circumstances, and the Wash 'n' Dash was steaming hot. Not to mention the fact that the last customer, whom Lou had to serve before she could close her register, was rummaging through her laundry bag like she had all the time in the world. I was considering hightailing it, when the door opened and Jordan came in with a duffel bag full of dirty clothes.

"Hey," he said when he saw me against the back wall, "you just moved to Paddler's."

I nodded, stomach tight as catgut.

"Yeah."

"Big change from the Bluffs, I bet."

"Yeah."

And he told me his name.

Just Ask Diane. That's a book Lou took out of the library when she was eleven or so and never bothered to return. It's a compilation of letters from Troubled Teens, and answers from 'Diane Reynolds, Teen Counselor' and syndicated columnist. Lou used to swing in the hammock, drinking Tab and reading bits out loud: tips for the unpopular and how to buy your first bra. "Wait! Wait! Listen to this one!" she'd shout, laughing so hard she spat out her soda. It kicked around after that, turning up every so often, and wouldn't you know, was one of the few books to survive the fire, its cellophane cover smeared with soot.

The first time I dreamed about kissing Jordan under the mosquito net and woke up covered with cum, I snuck into Lou's room and dug Diane out of the carton of salvaged books. 'Many teens panic needlessly when they have homoerotic dreams,' it said on page 147, 'but such dreams are seldom an indication of homo-sexuality. Your unconscious may be communicating your very normal longing to be close to someone, to have a special friend.' Close enough to bump my tongue across the ridges in the roof of his mouth, I wondered? Or did Diane mean the sort of friend who lets you slide a finger up his ass until the muscles crimp, like smocking on a little girl's dress?

"Mom," Lou said that night at dinner, "would you *please* tell Shepherd that if he insists on reading my books, he could at least wash his hands first?" Lou had a mean streak all right, but it turned out I only read Diane Reynolds once more anyway — the part about how homosexual experiences are not uncommon in adolescence, the 'just-a-phase' bit. Which was supposed to reassure me that deep down I wasn't *really* queer. Only from then on all I could think was, what if Jordan's 'phase' was already over and done with?

The woman spilled an arm-load of tangerine-colored sheets onto the counter. Behind Lou was a door leading to a little passageway, then the back room where Lou's gargantuan manager, Dickie, was spying on her over the top of his *Penthouse* magazine. I guess there must've been a pair of sneakers in one of the industrial-sized dryers back there, and something with a lot of metal, overalls maybe, because every so often there was a kind of scraping noise, then this hideous clump. Dickie — 'Moby Dickie' Lou called him behind his back — had a theory about laundry. "More than any other thing, laundry reminds people of the shortness of their time on earth," he told her when he hired her. "Be *cheerful*."

"I picked these up last week, and they're still covered with stains," the woman with the orange sheets said.

Lou shook out the folds.

"I'm sorry, Miss, what's your name?" Call them by their first names, said Dickie.

"Tami, with *one* 'm' and an '*i*'." She pulled a compact from her back pocket and stared at her upper lip, stretching it over her teeth to check her lipstick, then raised her chin in a tiny self-satisfied salute.

"The problem is, Tami, I can't see any stains."

Tami rolled her eyes and snapped the mirror closed.

"Here. Here. Here. Here, and here." Pointing with a painted nail.

On Lou's face was an expression I hadn't seen since she read *Lord of the Flies* and stormed through the house shouting, "KILL THE PIG! KILL THE PIG!"

"Listen, Tami with one 'm' and an 'i', our machines are good, but for some reason they've been giving us trouble with cum stains lately."

Jordan grinned, cheering her on, but in the back room Dickie was hitching up his Guiness-Book-of-World-Record jeans, lumbering through the passage with a look on his face like he'd always known Lou would come to this. When he reached the counter he circled the stains with a piece of chalk and scrawled the words *YOU'RE FIRED* next to them.

"What a creep," Jordan muttered and offered us a lift home in his Volkswagen. It was mud-spattered, with a motor that howled. I sat in back with the duffel bag.

We stopped at Münch's for a cone, parking under the neon face with its angst-contorted mouth, *I-Scream-for-Ice-Cream* sign blinking intermittently overhead. Jordan reached over and got a pack of cigarettes from the glove compartment, grazing Lou's arm. "Sorry," he mumbled, but there was something about the way he said it, a knowledge that his every gesture was a gift bestowed, that made the apology more like a bit of extra ribbon than anything else.

"I was thinking of going over to Lighthouse Park later." He shook the pack and a joint emerged from the hole, then he turned to me. "Do you smoke?"

I'm sorry if it sounds like one of the romances Lou used to write and send off to Harlequin, with their endless tendrils and cleft chins, but suddenly all the hairs on his right cheek caught the light from the late-afternoon sun and there he was, *haloed* for chrissake, and this shy little half-smile.

Lou snorted. "Where there's fire, there's smoke, didn't you know?"

I glared at her but she was smiling, a flirtatious smile I hadn't seen since she used to do Pepsodent commercials in the bathroom mirror, licking her lips and blowing kisses. She got out, tossed back her hair, and headed for the entrance, boobs bouncing around for everyone to see. Jordan watched her go, then turned back to me.

"What's *that* supposed to mean?"

"Nothing." I pushed the front seat forward so he couldn't see my face. "But anyway, yeah, I do. Smoke."

He came with the moths every night after that, scratching on our kitchen screen. In Lou's waste-paper basket, eye-pencil shavings began to appear, even as I was turning in front of the mirror, considering the option of a belt — trying to figure out whether, by some optical illusion, wearing my jeans so low they practically fell off my hips actually made me look bigger. I'd grown an inch that month, but up isn't the only direction. There's out and across to worry about as well, and my knees were still, proportionately, the widest thing about me. Chalk it up to bad genes, or maybe it was the business of girls 'developing' earlier than boys, but people had been assuming for ages that Lou, who was thirteen, two years younger than me, was my big sister.

The three of us would head for Lighthouse Park, where there's a bird sanctuary and a swimming dock, though hardly anyone swims there anymore since they made a sandy beach down the road from Paddler's. The lighthouse itself has been boarded up for years, but sitting at the end of the dock, Jordan said it was no problem breaking in. I'm not so keen on heights — or on break-ins — and I got the feeling he knew it, because he brought it up a lot. The same with the midnight swim business. Lou can only do the dog-paddle and she'd sooner die than put on a bathing suit, but Jordan wouldn't leave the subject alone. Lou didn't admit she didn't swim, of course, just like I didn't pipe up about my craven respect for law and order. We just sat there at the end of the dock, smoking dope and considering how to be. And meanwhile, the eye-pencil shavings, the white toes disappearing in black water, the tiny tantalizing splashes; I watched Lou edging closer and I knew: she'll get him. Boys like girls. And Lou was acting more and more like a girl.

Still, there were moments when I could have sworn Jordan was looking at me with that little half-smile, like he *knew*. Then one night, when Lou wasn't looking, he leaned over and whispered, "You know what? You have an eager neck." And I promised myself I would go to the top of the lighthouse if I ever got the chance.

225 steps below us, a kid in a yellow raincoat's hanging from the coin-operated binoculars at the end of the dock. *Naw!* screams a crow, *Naw! Naw!* and I have this flash of Lou, age five, standing at the top of the stairs in her flannel nightie, screaming *No!* as Daddy picks up his suitcase and walks out the door on the business-trip-that-never-ended. But Lou's back at the trailer now, cloistered in her cot-sized room after a fight with Mom, and I've kept my promise — shrugged when Jordan suggested jimmying the lighthouse window. I take another hit off the joint, thinking about dragonflies, wishing I had the guts to tell him about the documentary I saw at the science fair, back when I was around the kid in the raincoat's age.

I would tell him how they mate mid-flight. How the male grabs hold of the female's head, how she arches her body towards his 'sperm pocket'. How, attached at both ends, they spin through the air: like a Ferris wheel one minute, an upside-down heart the next. "The evolutionary reason for this configuration isn't clearly under-stood." That's what the guy in the film said. But up in the lighthouse it's clear as hell. I'm percolating at both ends, pheromones circling from my mouth to my groin and back again, and every time Jordan's eyelashes alight on the lavender skin below his eyes — that long slow way he has of blinking — I can feel my stomach hurtle to the rocks below.

"Think about the infinitesimal chances of a particular man selling me a pack of cigarettes in a particular drug store on a particular day," Jordan's saying. "Of my coming to earth at all, of his coming, of our coming at the same time, ending up in the same crummy town at the same crummy mall."

What about the two of us, I want to say, both at the top of the very same lighthouse, on the same evening in August, same fucking century, same fucking year? It's the kind of thing I'd always imagined lovers would say, but I'm not brave, or even stoned, enough to risk it. Not that the dope isn't strong. It is, plenty; I have to work hard to get the next sentence out before it shatters into a thousand fragments.

"That would be a great job, calculating the odds on miracles."

I know it's a moronic thing to say the second it's out of my mouth. But the weird thing is, when Jordan snarls, "That's exactly what's wrong with you, Shep," there's this funny little thrill that shoots through me.

"There's a million miracles every fucking second," he goes on, "only you're so busy doing the stupid math, you keep missing the next one."

The thrill ebbs. Suddenly I just feel muddled. "What?"

"Whaddaya mean, what?"

The next *what?* is what I mean, only I don't say it, because now the paranoia's really taking hold, and I figure the safest thing is just to shut up.

Jordan glances at me, a piece of dirty-blond hair falling across his face, slightly oily like it was washed not yesterday but the day before.

Then he looks down at the hole in his jeans, tugging at the fringe.

"The next *miracle*, you little twerp."

There's that same thrill again; something in me unclenches, eases back into his scorn. For maybe the millionth time that summer, I find myself wondering what if I hadn't set the couch on fire. Because I know it sounds crazy, but whenever I think about that, I have to practically sit on my hands to stop myself from making the sign of the cross and saying a prayer of thanksgiving. Only I guess with God it's the thought that counts, because now comes the biggest miracle of all. Jordan turns to me and says,

"Isn't it your birthday in two weeks?"

I nod.

"If I kiss you now, no one can ever say, 'Sweet sixteen and never been kissed.'"

I force myself to sit still, wondering if he's making fun of me.

"That seems like as good a reason as any. If you're brave enough to tell anyone the truth, that is." And he takes my finger and sticks it through the tear in his jeans. "You've been wanting to do that for a long time, haven't you?" His salty breath skates across my mouth as he catches my bottom lip in his. The sharp edges of shingles dig into my back. Then he cups my ass in his palms and pulls me close. And there we spin, a tangle of lips and legs, two dragonflies in the middle of the sky.

"Lucky little virgin," Jordan whispers into my neck. "So much to look forward to." And reaches his hand down, past the elastic in my shorts.

I leave him at his grandmother's just before dawn and head for the old house. Lately I end up sleeping there a lot. The trailer's small for the three of us, but it's more than that. A sort of exorcism, or maybe it's the dope, but the second I walk through the door, I find myself replaying the night of the fire. First the joint on the living-room sofa, then the walk down to the old stone wall. There was this pair of Japanese beetles, I remember that — and crouching down in the moonlight for an hour or more to watch them copulate. Next thing I know, I'm home, and Lou, Mom, and a bunch of neighbors are standing on the lawn in their pajamas watching the flames shoot through the roof over my bedroom. There must've been sirens and eventually fire trucks, but all I can see is Mom's face, pasty with tears.

Now, back in my old bedroom, ashes spiraling through the beam of my flashlight, I can just make out the sofa through the hole in the floor, a mess of naked springs and incinerated chintz, pitched forward like a drunk man vomiting over the curb. "Looks like it may have started here," the fire commissioner said, "does anyone smoke?" Dazed, Mom shook her head no. Lou was chewing the inside of her cheek furiously, but she knew the insurance depended on her keeping her trap shut. "I just had it upholstered . . ." Mom said. Then she saw her mirror, the one inlaid with satinwood that a photographer from *Arts and Antiques* had wanted to photograph for an article on mahogany, and her voice trailed off.

In the corner where the floor's still sound is my sleeping bag. It's soaked with dew, but I crawl in anyway. A few wire hangers are strewn about, and the brass base of a lamp. Everything else, the roll-top desk, the bureau, the bunk bed Lou and I shared when we were kids, has vanished through the hole in the roof or been carted away to the dump.

Usually, that's part of the ritual, to make an inventory of everything we lost. But tonight my mind won't hold still. One minute I'm thinking about fire — how it changes your mind about everything you thought was solid — and the next I'm remembering the last kiss, outside Jordan's grandmother's, a good-night kiss, sweet, like in the movies. And then I can't help it, I'm making the sign of the cross.

The next afternoon, having waited all day for Jordan to show, I work up the nerve to approach his grandmother. For hours, I've been watching her crochet a yellow blanket on her porch. It's doubled in size.

Our Lady of Root Vegetables, Jordan calls her, and when she shakes my hand, I catch a whiff of turnips and her palm is cold and damp as a cellar.

"I finally met your mother yesterday, poor thing," she says, setting down a pitcher of iced tea. There are three glasses, and for a minute I think maybe Jordan's inside, but then she says, "My sister should be back any minute. Isn't that a shame about your house."

And she begins to chat, twisting her rancid-butter yarn around a crooked finger, crochet hook darting in and out of holes. Gossip about the trailer park, who's been there as long as she and her sister, who is 'itinerant'. While I sip my iced tea, wanting to ask about Jordan, whose tongue has tripped along my spine, ask her everything she knows.

"We came for the view and that's what we stayed for, that and the swimming. Harriet, that's my sister, swims twice a day, down at the lighthouse. Crack of dawn and round about now. She had a wee stroke, poor dear. It keeps her fit." Her words unwind with every yank of her yarn and I want to ask her if the wind's ever dried someone else's saliva on her skin. "You'll have to meet my grandson. He's just about your age, maybe a few years older. Seventeen this past May. Oh, he's lovely."

There's a scab below my knee, a mosquito bite. I probe its edges, looking for a way in.

"Even when he was little, I knew what a heartbreaker he'd turn out to be. Those eyelashes, you never saw anything like them. You mark my words, I used to tell Harriet, he'll be a ladies' man just like his daddy."

"Still do, every chance you get," a voice booms out.

Flip-flops click against the roughened soles of feet and round the bend comes the tall bony one, pulling off her pink-rubber bathing cap with a resounding snap. One side of her mouth's hanging down her chin like an open drawstring purse, but it's the only untied thing about her; the sash on her terry-cloth robe is so tight it looks like it must've knocked the wind right out of her, and the towel round her neck is neatly tucked into the opening of her robe. On the bathing cap, two rubber daisies, yellow and white, bob in a sea of unpetalled centers.

"Harriet," her sister smiles, "this is Shepherd Mali. His family's the one I told you about whose house burned down. Over in the Bluffs."

The good side of Harriet's mouth lifts and lowers, more a push-up than a smile.

"I was just telling him a bit about our Jordan, thinking how nice it would be if they made friends."

Harriet looks right at me. "That's funny," she says, "I could've sworn you'd already met. Why just this morning, on my way to the dock, I saw two boys looked exactly like you."

For some reason I'm flattered by this; maybe it's the idea of a witness. The scab gives.

"Oh no, Harriet dear, you know Jordan's never up before eleven . . ." She pauses — one, two, three twists of yarn around a purple finger — then it's back to her favorite topic of conversation. "If I've told that boy once, I've told him a thousand times, handsome is as handsome —" She sees the trickle of blood sliding down my leg and jumps up. "I'll just get a Band-Aid," she calls and disappears through the screen door.

Harriet sits down next to me and drains her glass of tea, sopping up the run-off with a corner of the towel. I've got the feeling she's on the verge of saying something. Half of me wants her to, but the other half starts feeling superstitious, like this visit is the kiss of death. And then all I want is to get out of there. Harriet's chewing on a piece of ice. "He's a heartbreaker all right," she says, and I bolt.

Halfway down the porch steps, I remember about the Band-Aid and call over my shoulder, "Tell your sister . . ." but before I can get the apology out of my mouth, Harriet breaks into a lopsided smile.

"Sister? Is *that* what she told you?"

I can hear her all the way home, laughing so hard she sounds like the bird house at the zoo.

Back at the trailer, Mom's dressed, has been all day I know, in Dad's old plaid bathrobe, reading *House and Garden* in an unflattering light.

"Louisa's still at work," she says without looking up. "A Jonathan Something-or-other gave her a lift after lunch."

"Jordan?"

"Maybe."

"Mom, wake up! Lou got fired over a month ago," I shout at the back of her head. So where the hell have they been all day?

Under Lou's bed, I find a tin box covered with a layer of soot, her treasure box. Inside is a thing of mascara she's had since she was eight and a birthday card from Dad. Also, a dark-red stone from the beach at Lighthouse Park with an m-shaped crease at one end, like the line between lips. Once, I caught her kissing it; I still have the scar where she chucked it at my chin.

If I'm expecting a piece of paper saying where she and Jordan have gone, I don't find it.

Then, for no real reason, I put on a layer of mascara, first one, then another. It's old, probably six years or more, and I don't have a mirror. I can feel it wet and gummy on my cheeks. Outside are trees smudged against a violet sky. Inside is Mom running water into a pot. "I'm not hungry," I yell, remembering the two yellow daisies on Harriet's bathing cap, how she stretched the petals long and taut until they tore. Looking at me with her lopsided smile:

Loves me, loves me not.

It's ten or so and Mom's eating applesauce out of the jar when I sneak out. At the entrance to Lighthouse Park I hear shrieking and a splash. I tiptoe over to the binoculars at the end of the dock. *Bring distant points of interest within close range with the use of this machine,* says the little metal tag. I dig a quarter out of my pocket. The timer whirs and the circle of black falls away to reveal a circle of phosphorescent grey and a dachshund flailing through it, my sister, arms and legs igniting the sea, while he, naked on the raft, looks straight at me: *I'm the king of the castle and you're the dirty . . .* He dives, slicing through the water, a bright white spurt of cum, my resurfacing angel. And when he wraps his arms around her, I can feel his prick, hard, against my thigh.

Until the quarter drops and everything goes black.

I hear them leave, voices cold and wet under pulled-on clothes and the roar of Jordan's car. Up in a tree, the crow calls: *naw, naw.*

Just before dawn, the sky turns from black to electric blue to pink. 225 steps below, a fishing boat goes by, cutting a shaving-cream wake through the pinky-grey water, and an old sawhorse of a lady folds her robe neatly at the end of the pier and cannonballs off the high dive with a lopsided splash.

We meet on the way back to Paddler's.

"Well, Shepherd," she says, one lone daisy bobbing on her pink-rubber cap, "you and I certainly seem to keep similar hours."

The sand on the side of the road is wriggling with ants. We walk in silence for a few minutes, then Harriet says, "You know, I wish someone had told me when I was your age that in the end it doesn't make all that much difference." She doesn't look at me, but the harshness in her voice is gone. Something new, an embarrassment that is not unkind, makes me look up. She turns to me.

"Boys or girls, I mean."

Then she unwraps the towel from around her neck. "Here. You've got black smudges under your eyes."

Her robe falls partly open and I can see her wrinkled breast, bobbing like a buoy. She tucks herself back in, taking hold of one end of her sash with her teeth. "Now, wipe your face," she growls, and, with her good hand, pulls the other tight.

Dry Sherry

CAROL RAY

Carol Ray has had many different jobs and has spent long periods living and working abroad. She now teaches English and creative writing, writes fiction and some non-fiction, and lives in London with her husband and a ginger cat called Gus.

Mary Bruton drives north along Blackpool's North Promenade saying *I will not remember yet.* She says this in silence, her lips dry and smooth making the shape of the words, not daring to hear aloud the sound of her own voice. *If I speak now,* she thinks, *even to myself, I'll remember too much. I'm not ready. Later.*

And so, in the slow stream of evening traffic, Mary banishes the sensation of memory, and her inclination to look inward. She concentrates instead on the bicycle falling over in the wind over there, and the man with the little dog pulling on its lead. She glimpses, between the passing cars, Blackpool's golden sand disappearing at high tide, beneath a brackish sea. On her right, a tram rumbles past on its way from Fleetwood and as she slows down to traffic-lights, and the tram slows down with her, Mary sees it will have stopped at Bispham. But she looks away, reluctant to see, not yet wanting to think about Bispham. On her right, hotels line up in long terraces distinguished only by the size and access of the car parks in front of them. Some have switched on neon signs, attracting gloom like moths to a bare light-bulb. Everything, she notices, is in parallel lines: the terraced hotels to the promenade, the promenade to the tramlines, the tramlines to the horizon. She thinks she must have noticed this before, all those years ago, but today in the early evening gloom, willing herself not to remember, not until she is ready and concentrating on the present, the familiar seems unknown to her. This confuses then elates her, this feeling of otherness and difference; something she must hold on to, something she must grasp. Her knuckles are white on the steering-wheel. The traffic-lights turn to green and the tram on the other side of the road rumbles off southwards towards Lytham St Annes. She drives beyond the lights then manoeuvres the car into the middle of the road; she waits for a gap in the stream of cars; she is pressured by an urgency to get across the road. *If I don't go now,* she's thinking, *if I don't go now . . .* and she's cutting across the oncoming traffic and behind her a car swerves. Then slowly, carefully, Mary places the car between the white lines of a parking space.

And her heartbeat slows and she closes her eyes for a moment to listen to it. But she hears instead, *What am I doing here?* the words so loud in her head she might have spoken them. She pulls the rear-view mirror down to look into it. *I don't know, I'm not sure,* she says, misting the mirror with her breath; then she writes *Mary* in the misted mirror and smiles.

The Sea View Hotel is an end-of-terrace building, ostentatious in its velvet plush. It has seen better days; around 1965 Mary thinks, before the concrete soured and the salt had pitted the metal window-frames with rust. She's thinking now of 1946 when she and Tom had stayed in a Bispham boarding-house with white crisp sheets and starched pillow-cases. *There seemed to be more privacy then, less demand to be social — yes, I think that's what I mean — social, not sociable.*

She leaves her cases in the car and crosses the car park, the road, the tramlines, the promenade to lean over the wall. From a bleak horizon where cloud piles up like sediment, the waves are drawn diagonally to pound the promenade wall. The line of the sand where the waves pull back lies flat along the bottom of the wall. The horizon lies flat along the sea. Line below line, horizontal, parallel; the topography of Blackpool, a page in a school exercise book.

Mary pulls her suitcases along a dusty Axminster carpet towards reception. Two receptionists in seamless chatter, exchange information about room keys and days off. Mary listens carefully to the rhythm and inflexion of their words. Can she hear Oldham, and is that Burnley? The one who attends to Mary has nails so long her fingertips hardly touch the hotel register. She smells of Ysatis.

"Mrs Bruton is it?" She doesn't wait for an answer. "Oo — from Niagara Falls, I see. I've been there. It's lovely. I'm Angie. Let me know if you need anything."

Mary stretches her dry lips into a smile. "I was raised in Oldham originally," she says. "I used to come here for holidays." She turns her head as if these words with their acquired Canadian lilt had come from somewhere outside herself.

At this revelation, Angie lifts a barely visible eyebrow. "Really, I'd never've guessed," she says dismissively.

Mary smiles inwardly. *Well,* she thinks, *I'm not a* real *Canadian, am I.*

"I'm Accrington meself," Angie continues. "But Ginnie, now she's from Oldham, aren't you Ginnie?" as if that says it all.

Angie from Accrington withdraws behind her desk, polishing her nails, Mary feels, in contempt of Oldham.

She reaches her room at last, pulling her cases along stuffy corridors, past anonymous brown doors. Jack had recommended she stay here. "It's right good," he'd said when she'd phoned him to say she was coming over. "I've been to a few good do's there, I can tell you." She wondered how long it was since her brother had stayed here, and then it occurred to her he was probably talking about the food.

"Dear Jack," she says out loud to the roses climbing the trellised wallpaper in her room, "you were always up for a good do, weren't you." She tries on her old Lancashire accent since drowned with deliberate care in Canadian vowels. "When he sees me, he'll say, 'Aye lass, it's right grand to see you,' and I'll say, 'Sit down Jack and don't be so daft.'" Here she begins to laugh, sitting on the side of the bed, throwing her head back and laughing; and then the laughter dies because she's hearing Jack's voice from a long time ago, saying, *Now don't go thinking you're better than us, Alice-May, now you've got that big 'ouse in Niagara.* She hears the knowing emphasis, the implied disapproval, the bringing-down-a-peg, she-thinks-she's-better-than-us tone. Just like Angie to Ginnie at reception. She brushes her short white-blonde hair and goes to run the bath, leaving Jack and his Alice-May voice in the bedroom. Here in the sweet-smelling bathroom she can hear Tom. *Megsy, you're crazy. Why go back? You left all that behind years ago.* And back in mid-Atlantic rhythms, she says, "I know. But you're dead, Tom — three years now and everything has to be brought up to date."

*

The sun-lounge of the Sea View Hotel is a long hot corridor running parallel to the dining-room. The plate-glass windows are responsible for the sea view and sometimes the heat. Today, without sun, long narrow radiators burn your knees if you sit too close. Winifred and Frances Lord are settled in their usual place. A good view of the car park. They are here for their out-of-season-discount-weekend. Winifred crochets. It is likely to be a table-centre. It may end up in the Easter Monday craft fair at Rawtenstall Methodist Church. On the other hand it may not. Frances reads her latest magazine from Wisley. The Royal Horticultural Society are promoting auriculas. Neither of these activities distract Winifred and Frances from their true occupation.

"Well, Frances?"

"Well what, Win?"

"Did you see her come in? The one with the wheels?"

"The wheels?"

"On her suitcases!" Frances is prepared to drive Winifred mad.

"Well yes, Win. I did. And a very nice silk blouse she's wearing too."

"Not from round here, mark my words, Frances."

"Oh, I don't know about that. You can get very nice silk blouses in Marks and Spencer's these days."

Frances is not to be pushed into a corner. She is not going to be made to be definite by Winifred. They arrive promptly for dinner at six-thirty. The last sitting for dinner is at eight. They will stay the duration, eating slowly, weighing up the opposition, as Frances calls it.

"What opposition, Frances?" Winifred is laughing at her.

"Oh, do be quiet, Win, and get on wi' your soup."

The opposition comes in and takes her place by the window.

"Very nice," says Winifred.

"If you like that sort of thing," snaps Frances.

Mary is wearing black. A long gold pendant reaches almost to her waist. She touches it frequently, like a rosary. Winifred doesn't understand why Frances should object. She always said a little black dress was elegant.

"You always said, Frances, a little black dress was elegant."

"Not at her age. What I say is, 'colour after six when you're after sixty'."

"She's not sixty,"scoffs Winifred.

"I think she's here to meet a man." Frances risks being definite about this.

Winifred, looking at Frances across a small vase of freesias, wishes her sister were a man. She's thinking of Billy Weston now. She imagines him walking over to her and kissing her cheek.

Frances sees the colour rise in Winifred's neck. "Forget Billy Weston," she says, "he's dead and long gone."

But Frances' spitefulness keeps Winifred's memories alive.

Mary sits at a window table that looks through into the sun-lounge that looks out on to the promenade and across the tramlines. The day dips into the sea without anyone noticing. Jack is late; she knew he would be; he always was. She sips a pale drink glinting around ice.

"What's she drinking, Frances?" whispers Winifred. "Is it sherry or what?"

"You don't put ice in sherry, Winifred. What she's drinking is a *cocktail.*" Frances mouths the last word, furious with Winifred for making her say something like that.

Mary glances at Frances and Winifred, and knows they are talking about her. And she remembers that this is how it is here; the sidelong glances; the calculations of age and money. Nothing much has changed. She is relaxing now, laughter bubbling beneath the surface. She notices that the one in the heavily beaded turquoise top keeps looking her way, then leans across the freesias grazing their yellow-and-cream heads. She's calling the waiter, who looks over to Mary and then back again, all attention on the turquoise beaded top. She hears, "Tio Pepe, a type of dry sherry, madam," and the other one, the one with lipstick too bright, flickers a smile which settles on Mary like a butterfly.

Frances will hardly speak to Winifred now and Winifred is silently triumphant. She and Mary — they know about these things. She'd heard Mary talking to the receptionists; she'd heard her American-sounding voice and she'd heard the word 'Canadian.' She'd even heard her name — Mary Bruton — but she'd kept that to herself to use against Frances when the time was right. And then she'd put two and two together, hadn't she — as was her habit — and she'd thought, *You were a war-bride weren't you, Mary Bruton, and you escaped this place, like I might've done, if Billy Weston hadn't been shot to bits.* Her look drifts over to Mary, and Frances pretends not to notice.

★

The wind blows sharply from the sea, whipping up litter around Mary's feet. She and Jack are waiting for a tram that will take them to Blackpool Tower. Mary looks at her brother, younger than her by five years, small and scrubbed and dapper and always anxious. This is how he is now and a vision drops into her mind, of Jack at fifteen slapping his hair down with water because if he doesn't, *Me mates'll laff at me, I know they will, Alice-May.*

"It's good of you to stop over, Jack," she says. It seems the right thing to say — she couldn't have said anything else.

"Well, I wanted to. But I still don't see why, Alice-May, you couldn't 'ave stayed wi' me." He turns away from her then, pulling his collar up against the wind. She sees the rocking tram, miniature in the distance, about as far away as her youth.

Mary first discovered she was Megsy and not Alice-May on a tram from Bispham to Blackpool Tower. "Why do your folks call you Alice-May when your name is Mary?" Tom had said in that lilting Canadian which had wrapped around her, taking possession. "Because they're daft as brushes," she'd said, and they'd laughed themselves double. "Where I come from we'd call you Megsy," he'd said softly, stroking her neck, and she'd said, "That's daft as well," because Meg was short for Margaret where *she* came from.

And Mary watches the tram rattle her memories towards her.

She and Jack step out of the lift that has accelerated them to the top of the Tower. "I've not been up 'ere for gettin' on ten year," says Jack. "Changed a bit."

Mary cannot answer him. She would have to remember first; pull to mind the time in 1946 she and Tom had danced the quickstep to Reginald Dixon playing the Wurlitzer in the ballroom below; what a majestic sound that was; and Mary smiles to herself, remembering how she had persuaded Tom to come to the top of the tower to gaze in wonder at the seven miles of golden sand, even though he hated heights, and to remark on the fact that the trams go all the way from Lytham St Anne's to Fleetwood and back. *It's what you do, Tom, on holiday in Blackpool,* she might have said. And perhaps she would have said it with irony, but she doubted it, there being no irony in her at that time and at that age.

"Maybe Jack," she says.

And her brother says, "There's no maybe about it. There didn't use to be hotels and bingo halls strung out along the promenade then. It was boarding 'ouses at the back and stalls along the front; for candy floss and shove-ha'penny; surely you remember that, Alice-May." He's passionate now with disappointment. "And the beach — well, it's empty these days. Families don't sit with bucket and spade, and sand in their sandwiches anymore; it's out of the hotel and into the bingo hall, or onto the Pleasure Beach. That's what it is today." He walks away from her, pushing his way through the little crowd of visitors, his back bony and tight.

Mary looks down on to the streets of Blackpool and sees that it isn't only the promenade and the tramlines that run parallel, but other roads too, further back behind the hotels and then other roads crossing those, creating a street-grid, like in Niagara. It occurs to Mary that both these towns are alike: huge holiday board-games with their main attractions which you only get to see depending on the weather, or whim, or chance, if you didn't have a map. In one she was Alice-May, and in the other, Megsy. She'd made an exchange, that's all — a brother for a husband and the names they each called her by. And now? She turns to Jack and says, "Perhaps it's you who's changed, Jack".

"As to that, Alice-May, it stands to reason. But I know what I see."

She supposes that when she was Alice-May things stood to reason very easily. And when she became Tom's Megsy in Niagara, *It just don't figure, Megs* seemed a pretty clear way of reckoning. She thought she might have known who she was in 1946, more or less, the way one did then, at nineteen. *But now I am fifty-nine and alone, I must call up Mary — my secret self — because there is no one else.* Jack is beckoning her, wanting to go down. Mary looks up at the apex of the Tower, and a vision of crinolines pressed against the network of iron comes into her mind. *A hundred years ago,* she thinks, *Victorian ladies could see how the world could be laid at their feet by the skilful engineering of men.*

★

On their way down from the Tower, Jack and Mary stop at the ballroom. A notice tells of how it was burnt down and lovingly restored to its Victorian grandeur. There's whipped up plaster and gilt but no grand Wurlitzer to dance to, only a small electric organ at the edge of the stage. Frances, at eleven o'clock on this Saturday morning, is manoeuvring Winifred diagonally across the floor in a brutally precise foxtrot.

"Nothing much changed 'ere," says Jack with a kind of sorrowful satisfaction.

But Mary isn't listening. She's watching Frances deliberately trip up Winifred as the music comes abruptly to an end.

★

Mary walks Jack to his car and kisses his dark-veined cheek.

"It's been grand seeing you, Alice-May, but I don't know why you wanted to come 'ere, I don't really." He's petulant and wheedling. "And what's this calling yourself Mary for? I know it's your given name, Alice-May, but *I've* never called you that — no one has, as I can think on."

"That's right, Jack," she says. "No one has ever called me Mary."

"Well, there you are then," says Jack.

★

"So, you're not stopping," says Angie from Accrington as Mary hands over her room key.

"Well, you wouldn't, would you." Ginnie from Oldham impatiently moves the cordless telephone from one shoulder to the other. "You wouldn't stay here, not if you lived in Niagara."

"I'm going to Paris next," says Mary gently. Accrington and Oldham look up simultaneously.

"That's nice," they say flatly.

Paris, thinks Mary, *is evidently not a patch on Niagara.*

★

Winifred and Frances watch Mary leave from their usual place in the sun-lounge.

"*She* didn't stay long," sniffs Frances.

Winifred doesn't answer. She would have liked to say something to Mary. She doesn't know what — something about Billy Weston, perhaps. Only Winifred feels that if she had said something, then it would have been like going with her.

Next Year in Jerusalem

SHELLEY SILAS

Shelley Silas was born in Calcutta in 1959. She has been a TV researcher, casting assistant, fiction editor and motorcycle messenger. Her short story, Via Calcutta, was a winner in the ICA's 1996 New Blood competition. She would like to thank: Meg and Brad for comfort and food, the British Academy for financial support, the Silas family and Stella for endurance beyond belief.

'Funerals are pretty compared to deaths.
Funerals are quiet, but deaths — not always.'
Tennessee Williams
A Streetcar Named Desire

He has been sitting on the plane, on his last-minute economy patch of British Airways material, for four hours. Beside him, a woman, head covered with dark blue scarf, eyes never daring to glimpse even a breath of Danny. Her nails are bitten down, her mood is restless. When they serve dinner on disposable trays, she peels back the GLATT KOSHER piece of foil, eats quickly, meticulously. There is little room for mastication. Danny lets his unkosher repast remain hot and bothered under the film of aluminium for ten whole minutes before piercing the foil with his fork, watching the steam rise from the holes and evaporate into the consciousness of the 747.

She has chicken and rice, a bread roll. Vegetable margarine. She has never, to her knowledge, mixed meat and milk. An assortment of salad lounges helplessly in a square white plate. She chews the roll, eats the salad with her fingers, licks clean her no nail hands. And then she devours the main course. Danny is fascinated by the speed with which she condenses a fifteen-minute marathon into a five-minute sprint. She ignores dessert, a mound of red jelly with a peak of look-alike cream that any child would willingly whip off with a forefinger. But not this child woman. Her stomach is full, and not just from food. A baby is kicking her, from inside. He wonders how many she already has, waiting in a hot room for their mother to return. She is finished well before Danny starts his tin foil ritual. He can feel her eyes staring not at him but at his food. And he feels guilty. There is no GLATT KOSHER across his cover, no KOSHER to season her already partisan thoughts. He prods the meat with his fork, cuts it into easy to chew squares, dips it into gravy and pasta and lifts it to his mouth, satisfied with his ability not to spill. He doesn't eat his roll, wants to offer it to her but has second thoughts. After all, his kosher, non-kosher accountant's hands have touched the surface and she wouldn't want to indulge in someone else's religious depravity.

When the wheels smack the tarmac he is crying. It's because of the mood and the music and the emotions he feels deep inside his stomach. He doesn't want to cry, but he can't help himself. He turns away, looks out of the window at the patches of heat across the runway. He wants to run away. The woman in the dark blue scarf knows he is crying. She can see his body, a wave of anxiety, punching the air that is otherwise calm. He thinks of his brother, on another plane, close behind with Mother, Father, Uncle Jack and Aunty Esther. This trip is a covenant made by two brothers one hot summer's day. Danny has come to fulfil his part. Jacob follows in a carry-cot of wood. Tonight he will sleep in a borrowed bunk of metal. Tonight he will sleep alone.

Danny used to come here as a boy. Danny used to come here as a man. He has cousins two a penny, a worldwide web, an industry that perpetuates itself in its own image. There's Mooshon and Avi, Seemah and Michal, Tzippi (short for Tziporah) with her long blonde hair and Pacific blue eyes that never lost their sparkle. They used to roam the streets in leather sandals that skimmed the surface of the yellow soil. Danny first fell in love here, in Rishon Le Zion. It seemed appropriate, Rishon meaning First. Then, it was a small town, with a few shops and a bus station. He stayed with his father's childhood friend, a bulky man called Yossi, who drove a bus on hot city roads. His ever obliging wife was Meera, whose colourless voice would wake him in the morning as she wailed at her husband and children to "Get up before the sun sets." Danny loved the endless summer days, the coolness of the balcony at seven o'clock in the evening, the echo of neighbours, the rawness of the town and country. He would sit and gaze across the road at the corner shop, a hacienda-shaped building that Meera would go to every day for fresh milk and eggs and one of Danny's favourite ice creams, chocolate and vanilla wedged between two thick waffles. He fell in love with the owner's daughter, Tamar. She is married now, with three children and a husband who excites tourists with his cartoon sense of humour on bus journeys that take them into the lap of antiquity. Those were the days when he didn't care to think about ownership, about land, about rights and privileges and the cost of living. When someone else is paying, you don't ask for a receipt.

When he was a child, every time he left his grandmother to come here for a holiday, she would instruct him: "Go. Look for my son. Find him among the marble."

So he went in search of the uncle he never knew, who died long ago in his nursery years and was buried on the Mount of Olives. Or so they say. He had wanted to lie, to say, "Grandma I found him, I found Uncle Raffi," but she would come and see for herself and know that he was lying. They never found him and she never touched down on this land again.

"How can I have a holiday when I know he is nowhere and everywhere. How can I?" she would say, and crumble into despair. Now Danny calls it Et Tur, the Arabic name for Mount of Olives. He has learnt some Arabic, so he can show off his in-between state. He wants to be inside out, he yearns to belong, yet still be a tourist. But he cannot abide by their rules and so cannot play their game.

The woman beside Danny shuffles uncomfortably in her seat. She bursts bubbles of sweat into her hands, chews on her nails some more and waits for the all-clear from the tired stewardess. She is, it seems, at home.

The doors open and Danny's face is punched by the flow of hot wind. He watches the girl boy soldiers, guns hanging loosely across barely adult shoulders, and wonders how he will feel when Jacob is carried down, and laid to rest among the cold marble beds.

Danny passes through customs with ease, feels uncertain and decides to wait for his parents to arrive. He has a couple of hours so he buys a newspaper, a cup of muddy coffee and a chunk of poppy-seed cake from a stern-faced woman who takes his money willingly. When he thanks her in Hebrew, her face breaks into a thousand smiles. He is not just another tourist. He is one of them. Or so she thinks. He sees the woman with the dark blue scarf collapse into the arms of an older version of herself, surrounded by an assembly of children, all pulling and prodding and crying. And he smiles. He is reminded of an incident that happened to his Aunty Rifka on the Northern Line. Talking to a friend in her non-stop manner, arms flailing, tongue wagging, she noticed a young woman sitting opposite, dressed in a miniskirt, a white shirt and thin tights. Aunty Rifka told her friend that the woman looked like a whore, an undressed piece of meat that should not be flaunted in such a public place. She said the woman looked like a cow. She said all this in Hebrew. At Euston station, the woman stood up, straightened out her dress, looked straight at Aunty Rifka and mooed very loudly. Every time Danny sees Aunty Rifka she moos.

Danny calls his cousin in Jerusalem, says, "I'm here. I'm OK. I'm waiting for Ima and Abba." He hasn't used Hebrew words for mother and father for years. Perhaps his unconsciously collected soul is telling him something.

A ricochet of tangled words confuses his ears.

"I'llcomeandgetyouwhyshouldyouwaitthereonyourownitwon't-takemelongi'llbetheresoon."

"It's alright," Danny says. "I want to wait."

So he waits for the sun to set and the people to go.

His parents arrive with Aunty Esther and Uncle Jack. They are surprised to see Danny still at the airport, he looks tired and sad. His mother tut-tuts at the coffee stain on his shirt. She holds him close and wails into his chest. His father hugs him tenderly. His aunty and uncle watch, unsure of what they should do. Jacob goes on ahead. They will meet him tomorrow, on a hill in Jerusalem. The views from there are the best and when the sun sets the entire city bathes in a shadow of gold.

The journey to Jerusalem is made in complete solitude. They have hired a bus especially. A smoky blue bus with a driver who smokes unfiltered cigarettes and chews noisily. This is a private pilgrimage with no room for tourists. Danny's mother sits in the front, his father behind, his arm resting on his wife's shoulder. Every now and again both shoulder and arm go out of control. Danny sits in the back. There are no words between the family. A silent understanding will suffice.

Danny has travelled this road so many times, each one a different experience. Before the final climb to Jerusalem, in Bab El Wad, he grimaces at burnt-out bus shells, monuments to his father's past, sitting upright in mounds of earth. His father looks, then turns away. He does not turn to salt. He does not want to remember, yet he cannot forget. Then the climb begins, along the winding road, where the bus wheezes and pushes and tries to gain speed. Where the driver wheezes and pushes and tries to gain speed. The city lights shine in Danny's eyes and in his heart he feels a certain peace. Black figures walk the streets. Everywhere Danny sees men praying, men arguing, men eating. At home, the women wash and clean, cook and bake, make everything right for the men. Danny wonders where home is.

They drop Aunty Esther and Uncle Jack at a ground-floor flat, surrounded by raindrop plants. Danny kisses them goodbye, says see you tomorrow.

Their flat is built into the side of a mountain. One day, Danny imagines, they will fall from grace, slide into the arms of the bus queue below. From the balcony, past the rooftops and aerials is a vast expanse of desert. The air hangs still like a piece of fruit set in jelly. Someone has brought bread and cheese, milk and eggs, fresh fruit that will clear the cells. Danny stands under the shower for fifteen minutes. He stares at his Jewishness through veins of water, clears his mind and body of all that is past. Mingled with the water are tears. He doesn't want to cry any more. So he won't.

The family arrive one at a time. The door is left open so people come and go with no interruption. Danny stands on the balcony, smoking. He smells the cooked meat from a flat below. Children's voices simmer. Somewhere in the distance he hears a bird bark and a dog chirp. His mind is all confusion and altered states. One after another he stains his lungs with cheap nicotine. He counts the stars then counts them again. He makes shapes and gives them names, looking for a ladder for Jacob. He has to do something. He hears mumbled criticisms in throaty Hebrew he can barely understand. His mother waves to him. He reads her matriarch eyes. They are saying, "Please come in. Be with your family."

He squats on the floor, on the cold marble tiles, trying to speak but wanting to remain silent. He wants to be with his brother. If Jacob was here they would talk about work, about holidays and women and life after death. They feed Danny cheese borekas baked by his Aunty Rifka that morning. This time she doesn't moo. The pastry crumbles between his fingers. Ashes to ashes, dust to dust, he mumbles. Jacob used to like these. She tweaks his cheeks and makes him eat another. She ruffles his hair and gives him a plate with cakes and biscuits. When they are finally left alone, he shies away to his room, a small box-shaped pod where he will cry himself to sleep until he cries himself awake at the break of day. He does not want this day to end nor the next to start. He wants to cling to the here and now, to save the daylight of this August day. Of this august day. He shared this room with Jacob on their first trip to this land when Danny was a bar mitzvah boy and Jacob his elder. They talked all night about girls and sex and in the morning Jacob took his hand and led him through the broken promised land until they reached the Kotel. He remembers the tiny pieces of white paper, scrunched up and pushed into the cracks of biblical brick. Each one with a wish, a promise, an errand for God to carry out. God is just an errand boy, he thought, imagining a man with a long white beard cycling around the world on a push-bike, its bell ringing every time an errand was fulfilled. Once, Danny left a message. "Please let me get a bike for Hanukkah. And look after Mummy and Daddy and Grandma and Grandpa and Grandma and Grandpa (one for each side of the family) and Jacob. Thank you." He never did get a bike. He put it down to lack of communication and God's inability to read his knot of words. But if he is God, surely he can make sense out of the most mundane and lifeless and inaccessible? At thirteen Danny was still trying to find reasons.

It is morning now and Danny does not shave. He washes away the sleepless night from between his fingers, under his arms, below his buttocks. His nostrils are permeated with the smell of strong coffee, extra cardamom for his father. He smells burnt toast, perhaps fresh fruit too. He dresses in a suit. His only suit. A hand me down, dead man's suit. Jacob's suit. Under the thin grey linen, under the starched white cotton, his body breaks out in early morning sweat. He can feel the hot-cold sticky-dry but there is nothing he can do. He is a boy in man's clothing.

He stands outside the kitchen, stares at the dull figures clad in dark colours behind the frosted glass door. He can make out his father's bereft body, slumped over the table. His mother's old woman's hands arranging, always arranging, pouring coffee, buttering toast, in between snatched mouthfuls of food which she allows herself in a moment of guilty hunger.

They sit at the table, a fragmented family, the odd grunt invading the morose silence. His father ay-yai-yais, his mother gasps. His father gasps, his mother ay-yai-yais. His father rocks back and forth, his mother washes and dries up, making everything right for the men. At ten they stand outside, on the windy terrace waiting for Yossi to arrive in his rusty car with squeaky brakes and a wire hanger for an aerial. A few of the neighbours stand in a broken line. Danny interprets the wind that carries their thoughts. Through spring-cleaned curtains he spies eyes that pierce the brilliant morning sunlight. Everything is white and blue. In his mind at least.

Yossi's lips are curled down; he looks old and tired. He hugs Danny's father, kisses Danny's mother and stares at the boy in man's clothes.

The drive through the city is a curious delight. Danny's window is open and as they drive, the Jewish, Christian, Muslim temperature rises with Danny's North London mood. Hibiscus and oleander sweeten his sugar-free diet. He recalls a day when he came to the old city with Jacob to buy their mother a present (which she still has, a soft pink and green glass vase, dusted three times a week then locked behind the doors of a second hand cabinet). He remembers a particular day, a particular hour when they stood outside a run down cafe, at one of the entrances to the old city. They stared at this woman, with fuzzy black hair and a white T-shirt. He remembers going up to her and asking for her autograph. He knew Jacob was a fan, that he had all her records back home in their shared room with the cracked mirror and single beds. But Jacob was too shy to ask for anything. So he waited outside instead.

"Do you mind if I join you?" Danny asked.

"Sure," she said. "Take a seat. Want a drink?"

He sipped brown liquid from her can. If his mother had been here she would have reprimanded him, told him not to drink from other people's cans.

"Been here long?" she asked.

"I have family here," he explained. "I come every summer. We have a flat."

She offered him puffed-out pitta, hummus, tachina, a plate of pickles, carrots, and chillies, which he declined.

He gave her a postcard he'd bought for his parents.

"Write on this," he said. "I can buy another one."

She asked his name.

"Jacob. Jacob Bloom."

She scribbled her name, Roberta Flack, which he instantly smudged in a moment of overenthusiastic joy.

"Can I take a picture of you?" Danny asked. "With my brother then with me."

She combed her hair, wiped grease from her lips, took Jacob's arm and threw it over her shoulder. She sang Killing Me Softly as Danny took the picture.

On the way home they stopped by a cafe. Danny handed the autograph to Jacob, and Jacob handed him his thanks. They broke bread and wine over a vow that would never separate them. A covenant made by two brothers one hot summer's day.

They never told their parents about this daylight pact, only about their meeting with the American pop star who sang for her supper. Danny still has the photo, a faded relic of a past that no one can take away. He laughs at the flared trousers, Jacob's big hair and his own head of unpredictably tangled brown curls. That was then and this is now.

Now they reach the Kidron Valley. Past the Gardens of Gethsemane, to Mary's Tomb. As they pass he whispers, "Hail Mary full of Grace." He has a Catholic girlfriend in London. Her name is Mary. It's a month-old affair, too young to label a relationship, too old to call a one-night stand. So he settles for affair. He knows her Catholic guilt like she knows his. They have shared bread and wine, he has watched her take communion and next Passover, he has promised her, next year, she has said, next Easter, they have vowed, they will be in Jerusalem. They will eat hot-cross buns and matzo-ball soup, genuflect in church and wash hands in synagogue and sleep with a Star of David and a crucifix in their kosher non-kosher hearts.

Danny does not want the car to stop, wants it to keep sailing, through the streets, between olive trees so that he does not have to face the body of his brother, wrapped up in a shroud, covered with a prayer shawl, his injuries hidden from the outside world.

They arrive at the cemetery in a cloud of anonymity. Yossi parks the car and Danny's mother reels back in her seat, unable to look, to stare at the unbelievable sight before her. A shadow of mourners have gathered; family, friends, hands clasped in a circle of unity. Danny follows his father while his mother breaks the circle, stands near a dug out grave where she imagines her son soon to be, kissing the soil with his no speak lips. A constant hum hangs in the air until Jacob's body appears, Danny at his head, his father at his feet, a relay of men ready to catch him should he fall. Danny's father wipes his brow, clings to the body of his first-born child. Now he has two bodies on this big hill. Two bodies to read Kaddish for. One he can see, the other he imagines to be lying under the hallowed tombs and spat-on graves, picked at, like teeth, by someone else's hands. Before they lay Jacob to rest in a crib of earth, Danny whispers, "I brought you back. I promised I would," and leans close to his ear and strokes his brow under the shroud and tells him he loves him. This is what promised land means to Danny. The land that he promised to lay his brother in. There is a space beside his brother, untouched soil, shrubs beginning to puncture the surface. This is for him. For Danny. For the brother's brother.

"And I will come," he chants, "and I will follow you," he wails, "and I will sleep beside you again." Danny has kept his half of the covenant made by two brothers one hot summer's day. Jacob said, don't be sad for me, don't wail and wonder where I am. For I will be nowhere and everywhere. I will be up and I will be down. So they have tea and cake, and cry only small quantities of tears.

At night Danny sleeps under the stars on a mattress of feathers plucked from a duck who knew no better. He smells the roses, sees flashes of red geraniums on the balcony next door. He cradles his head in hands that touched the dirt from his brother's grave. He'll scrub them clean tomorrow. Under his nails the skin is torn from clawing his way through the soil to ensure his brother's head settled on a pillow of dirt. He is once again pulling back the shroud that covered the face that covered the bones and blood and so much more. He is spilling the arid ground into his brother's no-see eyes, lamenting for his kindred spirit and whispering sweet nothings into the ear that cannot hear yet hears everything. He is looking up at the sky, the moon and stars, the star and moons. His parents sleep and he breathes softly into the night. He breathes softly. He breathes.

Extract from

47 4F 44

BEN TEASDALE

Ben Teasdale *is 23, plays guitar badly, occasionally directs plays and films, and once had his thigh slapped by His Holiness the Dalai Lama. 47 4F 44 is his first novel and by God it shows.*

1. *Reader's Digest*

The end.

Then the blank pages before the back cover closes. This the only space we have left to inhabit — gates of ivory wiping to ebony as it nails its shadow down. And the blank space after the last heartbeat. And the notion of motion left in the stomach as the last train of thought terminates, still figuring some fading computation of aftermath. And it's only here and now, in the graveyard of stories, when it's all already over, my life passed ten thousand blank bastard pages back, that I finally find a first line:

The end.

Let me explain. This isn't just some excuse to short-circuit the story, to flash the spark I've been craving up my fingers and into my cranium and burn out the synapses that are pulsing with the morse-code from the muse. Listen to the tune — it's a falling cadence. The fat lady is clearing her throat and arranging her music on the stand. In seven days time the earth and every miserable mould and spore that clings to it will be instantaneously engaged in a free and frank exchange of atoms in the blank mandala of space. These words I'm bonding one by one in painstaking order will be free-associatively floating in a Dadaist cloud. This is my last first novel, the first last book and the only story you're never going to read — the point-blank blink-out manuscript. This is the end.

And so I'm taking control. I'm turning it around. I'm putting my foot flat to the floor and slewing straight into the oncoming dead-lights. I'm not going to eat. I'm not going to sleep. I'm going to plot each little death that passes until the trail leads me to the big one;

take it up to the deadline and poke a toe over. Fax back maps of the outlying lesions. Finish the story that started with a foetus forming in the word-womb. Supernova into the silence. Fuelled on glucose injections and filling facing pages in my pad with a pen in each hand.

THIS IS NOT A COP-OUT.

I know what you're thinking. That this is just an old man's bravado and beneath it I'm scrabbling for a way out, a back door. That the more you write, the less real you become (Shakespeare a shadow, flitting from folio to folio), and I'm sitting here groping for some kind of platonic suicide, trying to find a way to reach the point where I am erased into the text, nothing in me or of me outside the words forming, recorded, my evaporating life crystallised in ink as soon as it occurs by automatic hand. To shimmy round time; to sidestep death. Seven days and seven nights of uncreation to write myself out and write myself out.

Don't worry. I know what I'm doing.

This is the way the world ends — leaning in to listen to the sound of the late-night pencil smoothly worrying the page, the slow ignition of a continuous match being struck, the last night's last car burning up the road, the steady incendiary of the wheel on tarmac, slow cymbal describing itself in doppler, flame-phrase phasing, closing in on the sound, a tighter gap to lean to, lean in, touch paper, touchpaper, touch. And the pages swept up to immolate in thermals, descending as doves of ash, glowing sheafs slow-turning in the stack above my head; the crackle of the clatter of the keyboard, the sparks struck as I jab at the typewriter with dead-end fingers, the glint of flame winking in the nib of my pen; the thread-worm of fire writhing through the trail of my words, racing to swallow the final flailing syllable, flash up the barrel and open a book of fire in my face.

I know what's coming. And nothing in my fiction can change it.

So here it is: the death of the author and the author of death. Backwards road-movies, no-show murder mysteries and comedy holocausts. Junked codas. Cancelled stanzas. Home-movie mis-carriage and fourteen-chapter Caesarean. Maguffin catalogue, cubist rubrics, snuff autobiography. A book of hours, a badlands almanac, a retinal-scan bomb primed to pop if your read-speed drops; black box, maze of mazes, joke with no punch-line. Denouements only. Unbook. Life.

Well, hell, they always say write what you know . . .

Maybe the universe had hit the end of its elastic and was in a sickening nanosecond of freeforall before the long haul back of quarks and stars which would explain his inability to tell which direction the thing was happening in but the noise would not be this uijuhjuhjuujhnn bhbjhnjnhjhnn unless it had snapped altogether and that was the sound of gibbering space trailing the broken bungee of time as they accelerated off into nada.

There was space because there was a point and the point was a typed full stop on a page; and a page is a flat plane until you see it begin to bleed and realise that the full stop with its furry edges is soaking through from the other side and that beneath it the paper is crimped into subtle rifts and valleys by the pressure of the fingers of the hand holding it, and that the hand is squashed into thick folds of flesh by your own left hand clamped around it, and though there was space and forces operating in space it was like the page was a stage door hanging in the air between them and he could not tell if he were pulling or pushing it away and although they seemed to have it locked shut there were still dim backwards shapes seeping through.

There was definitely time because the blood was doing some tidal thing from the sea-meets-sky-line of the man's cut throat but as they stumbled and struggled he was unsure if his numbed right hand was desperately working to clear the pieces of paper from the man's oesophagus or shoving them in and in and further down. Torn strips of blood-soaked paper were hanging down his arms. If he was a child a frenzied artist he was trying to tear apart his papier-mâché doll before it was dry and get to the hollowness inside or stuff a solid core of newsprint into it.

His fingers jabbing for the back of the man's throat cleared a gap or filled one in. The man's right hand gripped him tighter or released its pressure. A semi-articulate gurgle started or ceased to simmer around his knuckles. The man's blood-shat eyes widened or contracted suddenly and as suddenly Time stopped all this fannying around as some canine reflex kicked in and the guy's jaws clamped shut on Lucas's hand.

Lucas whimpered. Let go. With slumping-back spine the man spastically, spectacularly sailboarded off Lucas's body. He rodeo-

"**A** friend of a friend, a dentist-phobic and compulsive gum-chewer since she was four, developed an abscess in one of her molars so painful that she realised she would finally have to get her teeth looked at. Not being able to get onto the books of any regular NHS practice, she went for the cheapest private dentist she could find. The 'dentist' in question turned out to be a medical student running the business from his digs in order to fund his extra-curricular habits; however, he assured her that he could give her a shot of local so apocalyptically huge that she wouldn't feel the slightest twinge during the extraction. Sure enough things went fine and she arrived home with a celebratory packet of Wrigley's already on the go. Oddly, no matter how much gum she spat out there always seemed to be a good wadge left in her mouth; and it was only when she tried to answer the phone to her boyfriend that evening that she realised she'd spent the seven hours since the dentist's calmly and methodically chewing her way through her own tongue."

When she was little, Cassie used to read and read and read. Under the covers with Molly and Golly and Debby the Dog and later (much later) with Matthew and Mark and Luke and Jim (she'd been going for the whole set, but had bottled out at the last minute, she said, having developed an unstinting aversion to telegraphed endings); in the booster seat in the back of the car and then on straight sections of motorways, the book trapped between the arches of the steering wheel; on trains, in planes and once on a roller-coaster; with blow-up books in the bath and magazines in the shower, soggy bits of page working their way down her arms and getting stuck in her hair. It all began in earnest with an illustrated hardback of the Brothers Grimm fairy tales she received from her Aunt Helen on her fourth birthday — having hit the end of the first story Cassie immediately launched into the beginning of the next, determined to find what had happened to the characters *then, after the end,* and leading her mother to make some involved joke about the puppy and the mirror. In her own mind, however, was the image of the little match girl, and Cassie was damned if each of her visions was only going to last until the match burned to the tip of the finger turning the page and she had to drop it. The search became

rode, clenching the fleshy tendony sinewy reins between his teeth, his left arm flopping madly in the air with the besmirched page flapping in his hand. Lucas tried to reel him in, making pained noises out of the side of his mouth, a door slamming in slow motion on his hand. The man collapsed onto him like an over-amorous aunt. Lucas staggered, his arm forced up and back in double-jointed salute. They began to dance a gravity tango. The head was cradled affectionately on his shoulder, nuzzling his neck and rolling its eyes. Lucas tried with infinite care and subtlety to prise open the mouth where his hell was brewing, slipping his fingers around the trails of paper that stuck out between the teeth like feathers of a half-swallowed bird, but only succeeded in producing a percussive flapping of lips gums and drool. He squeezed the man's nostrils shut, pulled away an umbilically obscene arc of slime. He rapped urgently on the man's forehead. He yelled something primal and inchoate and utterly inarticulately obscene.

The man blinked. Stilled. Blood was still washing down from the hairline slit in his throat like the overspill of a drain, guttering down around his shoes. The jaw went puppy-slack. Lucas's dead hand dropped. In the dark crib at the back of the throat, something was trying to be spoken, trying to rustle and rasp its way into the world. The man's eyelids fluttered. Lucas leaned in. A hand found his own. For a brief moment he was sure he could hear the faint pre-echoes of some pure sound trying to pass through the blockage, burn its way through the pulp of paper. He could feel the fingerprints pressing into his flaming palm, as if unspooling their whorl of information into his flesh. The eyes set in the mass of paper cuts that made the likeness of a face met Lucas's; something strange and subtle and tender and terrible passed into the eyes; passed through; passed out. Lucas began to lower him to the pavement. The mouth opened wider.

And opened out into a geyser of slick ticker-tape, alphabet confetti, raggedy speech-bubbles; as if a magician were pulling complicated handkerchiefs from his innards on a string of blood and bile, laboriously spelling out cut-and-paste hate mail; and Lucas stared, unable to look away, as out came words, words, semi-digested, rent and sundried, bleeding unred and black on fragments of paper, words pissing, shitting, fucking themselves on sound-compulsive, cumulative, as she devoured books whole, laying waste to libraries, devising her own reading schemes, working through books by colour and cover-picture and title and author and opening sentence, endings, plots, genres, themes, authorial stances, image-patterns, archetypes, structural analogies, rhetorical strategies, vocabulary-density scatter-diagrams, probability contingent feedback arcs, neuro-quantum virtual-fundamental projections. As soon as she could tell pheasant from peasant, tales began to tumble into one another. Characters from one book would peep around doorways in another. Names and events spanning the extreme edges of human history became entangled and interchangeable; texts began to talk to one another in a sort of trembling web, a neural network across time and space. It was as if she were not reading many different books but a muffled, semi-articulated version of one great, strange work, words and phrases and chapters of which were captured inside existing books like flies trapped in amber or particles from some vast exploded manuscript which tumbled through time into the open mouths of writer-oysters and became the driving, irritating mote at the heart of a wordy pearl. She began to realise that what she was searching for was the Story.

She corresponded with super-structuralists and Masai tribal historians. She trawled the Internet for interactive movies. She got an e-mail from an anonymous source who over the space of the last six months had established himself as a regular urban Homer saying that if she was interested in grand finales she should be at the corner of Portland Av. and Merrion St. at 5.17 a.m. on Saturday 25th, where, having briefed her best friend Sal on the assignation in case her correspondent turned out to be a bona fide last-chapter man, arriving five minutes early she saw, silhouetted in a wedge of sickly orange streetlight, the black outline of a young man murdering the black outline of a middle-aged man, forcing him to the floor to copiously vomit and haemorrhage.

Cassie had immediately backed into shadows and with very controlled, careful movements had pulled out her portable phone and dialled for the police, muffling each tone as it sounded. In a very calm, low voice she told them what she could see and where she was and then hung up, turned the ringer off, and determined to get the hell out of whatever trap or coincidence or voyeuristic

bitten pages, bog-roll snatches, gutter press, words fucking words fucking words fucking words. Words.

He was running down the pavement. Each step a car-smash. Piling it up. A postbox was careering towards him but that was wrong unless he were to feed it all in addressed to some random housewife. Your lucky shlucky numbers. He had to get a grip.

On a phone-booth. He lowered himself in. Went for the 9 and the 9 and the 9. Hit the 6 and the 5-and-2 and the top of the dialling panel with his knuckle as his finger buckled joint by joint. Nnnnnnnnnngggggged and hit 999 with his left hand. Got an LCD message saying if he wanted to get through to 652999 he'd have to insert some credit. Swore and hung-up-and-picked-up with his left hand and went for the number with his right hand and thought better of it and took the phone in his right whilst his left dialled with perfect precision and his right closed on the body of the phone and shot it out like soap from his blood-smeared palm.

"FOR FUCK'S SAKE! WHY CAN'T I—"

A quiet voice from around his feet was asking which service he required.

"AMBULANCE!"

"Please . . ."

Ring.

Ring.

Ring.

It was very quiet. The purr of the phone and the dislocated drum-and-bass of his heart up between his ears. Lucas looked out of the glass panels of the phone booth. Night had gone but nothing had come to fill the vacuum, the streets caught in an interminable moment of sleep-paralysis, waiting for the jolt to pass down telegraph wires and stir some limbs into epileptic light. This was not human time. Things didn't mean the same. He didn't belong here. He felt like a diver in a bell, lowering further and further and staring out into the city's fitful dream of pre- or post-human; everything colour-blind, corner of the eye, every stammer of wind or ricochet of birds' wings amplified with hallucinatory underwater clarity. The only absurdly lit-up thing in the gloom. Over by a low wall a frond of black dustbin bag waved languorously. A black-

scenario she had been led into. When she heard running footsteps receding into the distance she risked one last glance before legging it.

The young guy was gone and the middle-aged guy was in a spidery slump in the middle of the zone of light. As she turned to go she saw one of his shoulders twitch.

She froze.

She couldn't do this.

She took a few steps forward. She took a few more. She walked the distance and stood, skirting the edge of the pool of light. The pavement was slippy with dark liquid and a crackly sludge of fragments of paper. The man was face down, a black bendy bulk, like something glimpsed at the bottom of a fish tank. Then as she took a step into the light he was sitting up in a series of slow shuddering jerks as if cranked by machinery. She thought the face was a maze of seventy-year-old wrinkles then she thought it was the face of a twenty-year-old painstakingly cut to pieces. A trail of slewy liquid was hanging down from his half-open mouth, with tiny shreds of paper twisting and sliding down its length. A pair of eyes stared out at her as if from an immense and impassable distance. An arm extended with something in the criss-cross-cut hand.

She took it. It was a page of thick manuscript paper, the kind of paper that has weight and body and a wicked flexing edge and when stacked together is like a sheaf of guillotines. On it was a bloody half-handprint and blood in thick smears but also in score-marks and delicate feathering as if the edges had been used as an incongruous instrument of scourging or slicing. The page was typed or printed on one side and Cassie's eyes automatically began to scan the regions of words visible through the gaps in the map of blood. Three sets of words flashed in blinding succession into her head as if they had peeled off the page and launched up her optic nerve and in a frantic scrabble in her cerebellum Cassie found herself almost assembling a complete sentence of Story, a sentence which immediately dissipated into its component parts but left her crying out with the sheer vertigo of it.

The man was folding forwards. Cassie moved swiftly behind him and locked her arms under his armpits and around his chest, still clutching the page. She heaved and heaved him until he was nearly

bullet bird skidded low through the air.

He began to feel afraid.

Ring.

Ring.

<click> "Hello?"

He was running down the pavement. Like running down a lift-shaft. All human motion under the control of some fitful horizontal gravity. Head down, sickly hoping there is no elevator operational or counterweight slicing through the air the other way. Feet clanging and clanging and clanging in his cranium.

Stumbled out into ground floor. And found gore but no body.

"W—"

There was the pavement and there was the lamppost and there the in-out-slake-it-all-about and there the unsteady image of the man's shape, as if a hanging ghost in the retina or sweated in sleep through sheets of bitumen or bled out his dimensions so only this shadow remained. But no body.

Lucas swung around. Side-streets and shadows. Swung a slow dark sparkle and fizzle of sick quicksilver up across his eyes and a shaky maze of veins, side-streets and shadows. He began to feel the overwhelming need to pee. He turned again. Nothing. Nothing. Then suddenly and as if from nowhere he seemed to have developed this 180° blind spot — a blind swathe — that he couldn't shake off and he knew with absolute certainty that there was someone or something standing in the half of the world that was cauterised out of his brain. He swung around. He swung around. He swung around. A noise. He swlipped in the shit and crashed arse over tip into someone else's innards.

He scrabbled in the scrabble. Front scrawl. Up-strokes and down-strokes. Someone was trying to spell something out to him but he was turning his nose up and giving it the cold shoulder. Flourish and scroll. Hack and splutter. Grub Street. He closed his eyes. He closed his eyes but he couldn't keep out the sound swelling at the back of his brain, an idiot lung filling and collapsing and reeling out empty phrase after empty phrase, sawing back and forth, the endless repetitative patter of some mindless thing that had been trailing him for long silent months and had finally picked up

upright, then began to drag him backwards, labouring along the pavement a few scuffling steps at a time, leaving a paper-chase of scraps and blood. He was incredibly heavy, and there was some strange elastic quality to the weight as if she were pulling along not only the man but some dense bobbing shadow hanging down from his slender upper body. As they passed out of the streetlight his head curled forwards into his chest and what with his legs trailing together like a tail and the fluid glistening on his skin Cassie had a momentary flashing vision of an embryo or foetus and it was only then that she noticed how grossly distended his stomach was, the belly bulging disproportionately out of his shirt. As she made it around the corner, with three streets still to go to her car, a button flew off and bounced three times along the kerb and then off and she heard halting feet and a half-articulated sound.

The summer before her final year at college Cassie's cat had been dying of a throat tumour, eating nothing and turning feral and hiding in the deepest bushes he could find, staring out with unrecognising eyes. They had brought him inside and tried to keep him in a basket to protect him from the flies and heat but periodically he would lurch into action and make sudden desperate drunken dashes for the door, swaying crazily and crashing into chair legs. Gradually he had settled down and let out his nine lives one by one, each time a breath followed by a long, long period of stillness in which it was impossible to tell if he was still hanging on. Cassie had sat with her mother and watched the cat's flank for several hours, both pairs of eyes increasingly unable to distinguish movement from stillness. Finally when her father returned home he had lifted one end of the animal and it had hinged up like a plank, utterly stiff, a plaster cast of a cat. Cassie had seen the moment when life turned to death and a body turned into an object and this was not a body but an object, plank-dead. She let it hinge to the floor and turned and ran.

A siren started wailing somewhere nearby. That would be the police careering in. She couldn't make out if there were footsteps behind her or not but any minute now the place would be swarming with cops and she would be safe. She would run straight into a patrol like a sprinter crossing the finish line and she would tell them in a big ball of adrenalin what had happened and show them the

his scent and was baying the air now in borrowed accents, in glib unthinking singsong, aping the things it had heard, punning with no meaning, gaining on him, closing in on him whilst he slipped and slid and floundered in a pool a puddle a miasma of words. (Putting words in my mouth. Taking them right out. Can't stomach it. Won't swallow the story make him eat his own he really writes from the gut EVERYONE'S GOT A NOVEL INNEM hee haw hee ha hoo hoo oh don't I'll split my sides oh God I'll epistle meself I swear it'll be diaryhoea all over again please stop Stop STOP.)

He closed his eyes. He closed his eyes.

Suddenly he was illuminated. Something big wailed around a corner and caught him in a sweep of blue light. His eyelids like vellum. Stopped. Lost interest in wailing. He stopped struggling. A door. Footsteps. Steps stopped. A voice.

"Get the stretcher!"

He was trying to explain that whilst a stretcher seemed like an outstanding plan in principle in fact it had been him his very same self who had made the call that had brought them here and that this was just an unfortunate albeit somewhat ironic crossing of their various wires given that the personage whom they really should be attending to with some not inconsiderable degree of urgency was currently located in an indeterminate state at an indeterminate site elsewhere but in all likelihood not too far from their current locale and no, really, please put that needle away but his eloquence was somewhat hampered, his panache somewhat marred, his communicative *élan* to a certain degree compromised and/or ruptured by the paramedic's fingers trying to clear his airways. Then the oxygen mask clapped over his face.

(What the fuck have they given m— huh?)

Someone was ripping his shirt open. He felt two lubed metal plates pressed cold against his chest.

(Oh Jesus.)

"Stand clear!"

He wasn't entirely clear what jffffffffffggggggggggggggggggkkkkkkk lllll m xx.

Ffa-dumm. Ffa-dumm. Ffa-dumm.

"That's a pulse! We've got a pulse! Let's go!"

Had there been present, in the back of the ambulance, as Lucas

body and show them the page and they would take the page. They would take the page.

She couldn't let that happen.

She broke her rhythm and snatched a glance behind her. No one was following. The guy must have scarpered. She turned into the street where her car was parked. She could just drive home now but they had the record of her call and might already have traced her address from the phone company and be waiting for her and would take the page. She got in the car and started the engine and began to pull away. What she needed was a copy. Now. Whilst she didn't have to account for her movements.

She turned a corner as a police car flashed past a side opening. She turned away from what would be her route home towards a small street with shops on. Nowhere would be open. She saw a sign.

Somewhere would have to open up.

I was panicking, officer, I didn't know where I was going . . . she swung the wheel and the beam of the left headlight shunted the shop window into a pointillist scintillation of shivers and shards before snuffing itself out and scattering flanks of stars and glittering adzes halfway across the patterned carpet. An alarm bell began to sound. Cassie slid out the passenger side and waded atonally across the room. She found a switch behind a counter and yanked up the lid of one of a row of photocopiers against the wall, put the page in face down and hit a button. Freezer light spilled up into the room, and in the second it took to make the copy Cassie could see, through narrowing pupils, both sides of the page illuminated into a single flat plane, and burning black through the layers of blood the spidery arabic of printed words. She turned the page over and hit the button again. The words were the right way round but the illumination was too brief to make any sense of them. She leaned over to the number panel and pressed 9999 and hit the button, then, one hand shading her eyes, stared at the page, eyes trying to locate and relocate as it slowly strobed the room between darkness and blinding halo, slewing out an infinite loop of keeling shadows.

"Seven days . . . I'm not going to eat. I'm . . . into my cranium and burn . . . and the only story you Dadaist . . . This my last first novel . . . gates of ivory wiping to ebony as it nails its shadow down. And . . . Listen to the tune . . ."

was strapped and plugged and slotted in, someone sufficiently trained in the breath moisture distributions of vocal phrases in the vulgar register, they might have deciphered in the hurr-on-perspex pattern above Lucas's face the repeated and increasingly tranquillized semi-vocification of the word "fuck." That not being the case, his communiqués remained unheeded.

(Lie back and gag on my gags whilst they rush me to Causality . . .)

With a jolt Cassie was aware of the alarm bell still blaring. She snatched the copies from the tray and pulled the page from the machine and hinged the lid down and got into the car and went into reverse.

As the sound of the car pulling away dwindled the copier continued to churn out images of a smear of blood on the platen glass, a mounting pile of Veronica's napkins filling the tray and spilling onto the floor, until it was out of paper and just wiping light over the image, running on empty, baulking at the sight, trying to wipe it clean.

For days afterwards people swore there was a ghost in the machine.

Comedian

MARK TILTON

Mark Tilton was born and grew up in Blackpool, Lancashire. For some years he was singer and guitarist with punk thrash band The Membranes. He has written, directed, edited and acted in several award-winning films. Mark now lives in London, and is working on a novel about school-yard violence and the Blackpool underworld.

He would like to thank the British Academy for financial support during his time at UEA.

I come home from work mid-afternoon, about three o'clock — a bit earlier than usual — and when I walk in the door I can smell something, like something's out of order. I'm in the hall; I shout Jackie, my wife. No reply. I think, "Hang on." It's like something's burnt, like that electricky smell you get off toy train sets when you're a kid, or like when you forget and put a pie still in tin foil in the microwave. I follow the smell upstairs to the bathroom and, when I look inside, there's my bath (she always had a hot bath ready for me when I got home), only the electric fire's been chucked in. It's plugged in and there's black and grey oily scum floating on the water.

I go downstairs and her coat's gone, so I dash up to the bedroom (I'm up and down like a yo-yo) and the bedroom's a mess, like a bomb's hit it. The bedroom window's open and, when I look out, all my clothes are strewn all over the garden. There's a pair of my underpants hanging on the kids' swing.

I'm shaking, so I sit down on the bed and look around. All the drawers are emptied, and most of her stuff has gone. She's left the nightie I bought her (probably dirty.) Then I see she's left the hat I got her for the wedding. I remember thinking she'd never wear it, only at the wedding, so it makes sense she's not taken that. But then I realise; everything she's left is everything I ever bought her. She's sorted it all out: clothes, perfumes, jewellery . . . and sitting on the dressing table, pride of place, her rings — wedding and engagement.

Now if something goes wrong you do something about it. We'd had a row the night before 'cause a bloke at work told me he'd seen her with Charlie Hook. I told her what he'd said, and she'd gone over all white-faced and denied it. A lot of blokes would've hit her, but I never. I never hit women. Only the lowest scum hit women.

So I ring Charlie Hook. No reply. Fucking comedian. No — that's what he is. He does a spot down the Conti most Fridays: magic and comedy, all one-liners and sawing girls in half. That's where we got talking to him. A smarmy little git, all fake tan and that. His face isn't brown — not healthy like he's been working outside — it's orange. Never stops smiling. Jed reckons he's had a face-lift, plastic surgery, and I'm thinking, "He'll need it when I get hold of him. I'll wipe the smile off the back of his neck."

★

I was crying the whole time I was packing my bags. I felt sick. I was a mess. And I nearly stopped myself a couple of times. I nearly put it all back in the drawers and was ready for pretending it was just a normal day. Maybe that's why I threw his stuff out the window — so there was no going back. Each thing I threw out, I felt a bit better. Made me think it should be him I was throwing out.

I made that house. I made it our home. It meant everything to me, and I was chucking it all away. I thought about the kids' things up in the loft, daft things I'd saved from when they were little babies — like their first little shoes — and how I'd have to leave them behind 'cause I'd never find them in time. Their tiny shoes.

I was sick, crying and everything. I hadn't planned it. I'd started running his bath earlier on without even thinking about it. I'd done it so many years, it was habit. When I went back it was near to over-flowing. Time was getting on for him coming home, and I wanted to be out before he got back, but I still plugged in the electric fire so it stood there glowing all red in the steamy bathroom (he always told me not to have it in there 'cause it was dangerous). Then I picked it up and threw it in the bath, just like that. It was all crackling and fizzing. I thought to myself, "I'm a dangerous woman, Peter Banham — and you're a boring man."

★

I go round for Ken and tell him what's going on. He keeps telling me to calm down, like I'm overreacting because my wife's left me for some arse'ole, fake-tan entertainer. I can feel my hands round Hook's scrawny little neck. I'm well up for it. I mean, there's right and wrong in this world and it don't take a genius to spot the difference. This was all wrong. Right from the start. All wrong.

Ken finally admits he knows where Hook lives and we set off over there. I keep leaving Ken behind and then keep having to wait for him to catch up 'cause I don't know where the fuck we're going. And all the time Ken's saying, "You should talk to her. Don't do anything you might regret," and all that shit.

I pop back into our place on the way and pick up our Brian's baseball bat from the garden out the back. I make Ken wait out front 'cause I don't want him to see all the mess. When he sees me marching down the path with that bat in my hand he gets all reasonable, like he's going to talk me out of it or something. He says if I don't put the thing down he won't show me where Hook lives.

I say, "You're supposed to be on my side!"

Next thing, Ken plonks down on the garden wall, gets his tobacco and Rizlas out and starts rolling one up like we've got all sodding day.

Now Ken'll never match me in the stubborn stakes, but I'm not going to spend an hour swinging my legs on the garden wall, so I chuck the baseball bat on the front lawn and we're on our way.

It's all whizzing through my head, what I'm going to do, what I'm going to say — and I'm not planning on much in the line of parley. It's taking forever to get there and Ken's looking well nervous and wanting me to slow down and I see Acacia Avenue and say, "Ken. We've been this way before, Ken." I know he's doing what he thinks is best, but he's taking me round in circles hoping I'll cool down and all the time I'm getting more and more het up.

So, right then, I stop. I put my hands on Ken's shoulders, and ask him very polite, "Look, Ken, do you know where this bloke lives?"

"Yes," he says.

I look him right in the eye. "Where?" I says.

"Ferntower Close. One of the cul-de-sacs off the Park Road. Thirty-four."

On my own, I get to thirty-four in no time — all that pissing around in circles. I knock on the door. No reply.

Standing on one of the bins, I leg over the side gate. Suddenly I recognise the place 'cause I'm sure I'd done the dustbin round there a few years back, only it's not so run down as I remember it.

I get the feeling they're in, like I'm not too late, and I peer in the back and look in on the kitchen . . . and there's this little whiff of steam coming off the kettle.

★

I got the kids out of lessons early and they were surprised to see me. I'd pulled myself together on the walk over there and I was trying to be as calm as I could. We got to the school cloakrooms. It was all quiet, nobody around. All the time I was thinking Pete would be after us if we messed about, so I tried to hurry them up without getting them all upset. I told them we were going to Manchester to visit their gran and grandad, and they weren't very pleased. Brian's fourteen now and Liz is eleven, and they're at that age. I looked at the two of them — and suddenly it was like I'd never set eyes on them in years. They were strangers to me — all grown up. And everything about them — the way they moved, the way they talked — had something of Pete in them. Brian especially. And I wondered how they were going to be. They worship their dad, and I was tearing them apart.

Liz asked if her dad was coming, and I made some excuse about how he'd have to work an extra day because of the Bank Holiday. Then they wanted to know where their clothes were, and Brian started going on because I hadn't packed any of the right things and I just couldn't hold it in any more and I started to cry.

Brian went all quiet. And then he really surprised me. His eyes went all soft like he was going to cry as well, and he put his arms round me and gave me a big hug, and then he started helping Liz with her coat — only she hated that 'cause she's all grown up, but at least he got her moving. Right then a load of lads came barging in, laughing and joking. And there we all were — the three of us trying to pretend it was all OK.

*

I know they're home. The tell-tale signs. Fresh soapsuds in the kitchen sink. Sort of things Jed goes on about when he's burgling. Makes me feel seedy, like I'm like Jed, like I'm letting myself down, but I snap out of it — I don't need reminding why I'm there.

I rap on the window of the kitchen and this little girl, about five or six, wanders through and looks all scared. Curly brown hair, a bit like Lizzie. She dashes out again calling, "Daddy," and this bloke comes down in a blue dressing gown, all cautious. I don't recognise him at first. He must wear a rug, 'cause he's all bald and nervous.

The sight of him sparks it for me. I smash the glass in the back door with my bare fist. But I can't get the door open. He comes at me, whacking at me with some pathetic kitchen utensil, a rolling-pin or something, and I'm struggling to get through the door, broken glass and blood all over the shop. He whacks me on the fingers a few times, but I don't feel a thing, when I grab hold of his arm, prise the rolling-pin out of his fingers and start ramming it down his smarmy gob. All the time I can hear this high-pitched screaming, and then I realise the screaming's me. The kid's standing in the kitchen, watching, and I'm shouting, "Jackie! — Jackie!" He's halfway out the window by now, so I drag him right the way out, pull him up by his dressing-gown, and the thing falls off. He slips through my fingers and he's rolling around naked on the muddy grass — this little orange man smeared in mud and blood. I grab hold of him by the throat and look him right in the eye and say, "Where's my wife?" and he just wheezes, all starey-eyed and floppy — then he stiffens and knees me in the bollocks. I buckle with this fucking draw-string pain running from my balls up to the top of my guts, and he must have head-butted me then, 'cause next thing I know my nose is spurting and I can't see a fucking thing. He's lying on the floor. I can hear him blubbing. I can't see, but I can hear the house is dead. It's just me, Hook and the little girl.

*

On the train, none of us could speak. It was all hanging over us. I was wondering if I'd made a mistake, but then I thought about all the stuff behind us.

They kept asking me if their dad would be all right and when they'd see him, and if they could phone him when we got to Manchester.

Something in me wanted to turn them against him. I wanted to say how everything about him is always under control and dull and shabby, and how he never says thank you, and how he never washes his hands properly, and how I was sick of being forgotten until bedtime, and how we always had sex the same way, and how he thinks it's soft to say 'I love you', and how he never wanted kids in the first place and if it wasn't for me they wouldn't even be there.

But they wouldn't want to thank me for being there, would they? So I told them their dad was a good man and he was doing his best, but it wasn't really working out, and we needed some time apart to try and make things better.

But I knew I was never going back.

When we got near Manchester, it was getting dark. Liz was asleep, holding on to my arm, and Brian was sitting across, looking out the window. I could see his reflection, and he looked like he was trying not to cry. I leaned over and I put my hand on his. But my hand just lay there like it didn't belong. I couldn't tell if it was just me, or if it was both of us, but the longer I left it there the worse it felt. It's terrible, but I was relieved when he pulled his hand away and rubbed his eyes like he was tired.

We looked out the window, and the backs of all the houses were going by. Some of the curtains were still open, and we could see into the back rooms: people watching telly, or sitting down to eat their teas.

Brian said, "I don't like Manchester."

And I thought, "Neither do I, my love. Neither do I."

Lapsang Souchong

CHARLIE WATSON

Charlie Watson *left a career in commuting and computing to live first in Paris and later in Texas, where he married, attended university, and began to write. He has never been to Paris, Texas.*

Characters: Waitress
                    Eddie
                    Edward
                    Man

A café, perhaps suggested very simply with several small tables, each with two or three chairs. Only one table is available — the others are occupied by dummies, except one which has not yet been cleared.

At rise, the WAITRESS *is resetting the one free table. Her movements and appearance suggest weariness. She steps back to check her work. She shrugs her shoulders.*

WAITRESS Aaah.

She begins clearing the uncleared table. Just when she has a few things stacked up, a bell jangles off-stage, and a door can be heard closing. She dumps the debris back on the table and bustles over to greet EDDIE, *who enters stage right.* EDDIE *is casually — even a bit scruffily — dressed.*

WAITRESS Just one?

EDDIE *(Looks around; smiles)* Yeah, I think so. Just one.

She leads him to the free table.

WAITRESS There.

EDDIE Great.

As EDDIE *sits, the* WAITRESS *exits stage left.* EDDIE *pulls out a newspaper, and starts reading. The* WAITRESS *returns with a menu, which she drops unceremoniously on his table.*

EDDIE Thank . . . you.

She goes to the table she was clearing as EDDIE *came in. Once again, the bell jangles and the door shuts just as she has picked up a stack of plates, glasses, and cutlery. With a sigh, the* WAITRESS *dumps the stack back on the table. This time she crosses to meet the smartly dressed* EDWARD.

WAITRESS Just one?

EDWARD Just one.

The WAITRESS *turns towards the tables, and realises that none of them are free. She turns apologetically back to* EDWARD.

WAITRESS I'm sorry, there's —

EDWARD Well, how about there? *(Indicates the empty half of* EDDIE'*s table, and walks over without waiting for any response from the* WAITRESS. *She shrugs. Now, to* EDDIE:*)* Mind if I join you?

EDDIE Er . . . no. 'Course not.

EDWARD *sits opposite* EDDIE, *who smiles, then looks down at his menu.*

WAITRESS I'll get you a menu.

She rushes off, stage left, then returns with a menu for EDWARD. *While she is fetching the menu,* EDWARD *looks curiously at* EDDIE.

EDWARD Thanks.

WAITRESS *(To* EDDIE*)* Have you decided?

EDDIE Mmm. Pot of tea, please. Lapsang souchong.

She scribbles this down, then turns to go, but is stopped by EDWARD, *who hasn't even glanced at his menu.*

EDWARD Mmm, lapsang souchong. I'll have the same.

WAITRESS *(Scribbles this down, too. Looks at* EDDIE *and* EDWARD*.)* Two lapsang souchongs.

She exits left.

EDWARD That's a nice tea.

EDDIE Eh?

EDWARD Lapsang souchong. Nice tea.

EDDIE Yeah. Yeah, it is.

EDWARD Unusual. Do you always drink it?

EDDIE No . . . well, sometimes.

EDWARD Me, too. Just the same. *(Pause.)* Sorry, I didn't catch your name. *(Extends a hand, which* EDDIE *accepts unenthusiastically.)*

EDDIE Eddie.

EDWARD Eddie! Well . . . that's my name. Edward. And you're an Edward, too.

EDDIE Well, yeah.

EDWARD Not so common these days.

EDDIE No.

EDWARD And the few of us there are get divided up into Eds and Teds and Eddies and Teddies. *(Laughs.)* Have to stick together.

EDDIE S'pose so.

EDWARD What's the rest of your name?

EDDIE Look, I . . . oh, what the hell. Lane. Eddie Lane.

EDWARD What? You're kidding . . . your name's Lane? L-A-N-E?

Pause.

EDDIE *(Nods sceptically.)* Yeah.

EDWARD That's absolutely amazing. So's mine.

EDDIE *(Slowly.)* You're Edward Lane?

EDWARD Yes!

EDDIE Well . . . good. I mean, so what?

EDWARD Well, what a coincidence! We're not just in the same town in the same café at the same time, but we're sitting *at the same table!*

The WAITRESS *reappears, with a tray covered in teapots, milk jugs, cups and saucers.*

EDDIE Huh. S'pose so. *(Under his breath:)* I was here first.

WAITRESS Two lapsang souchongs. *(Begins unloading the tray.)*

EDWARD Yes, you were. Edward the first and Edward the second!

WAITRESS Anything else?

EDDIE No, thanks.

EDWARD No. Thank you. *(The* WAITRESS *goes across to the uncleared table. As the conversation at the table continues, she picks up the stack of dirty plates, and exits left. A fair amount of clutter remains on the uncleared table. Now, to* EDDIE:*)* So . . . so are you from around here?

EDDIE Lived here all my life.

EDWARD You have? *(Pause. Looks carefully at* EDDIE.*)* Are you sure you're not having me on?

EDDIE What? Why?

EDWARD Because I've lived here all my life, too. I was brought up here.

EDDIE Well.

EDWARD No, you're kidding, aren't you? *(Accusing:)* You, you guessed my name, or someone told you, didn't they?

EDDIE No, they didn't. No one —

EDWARD Look, you might as well come clean. It's not clever, you know, pretending to be someone you're not.

EDDIE I am *not* —

EDWARD I mean, some people would be really offended.

EDDIE *(Annoyed.)* Listen —

EDWARD So you're lucky it's me — at least I can take a joke.

EDDIE Look, I'm not pretending to be anyone. I am Eddie Lane, OK?

EDWARD Huh. You're in too far to back out. That's it, isn't it?

EDDIE No!

EDWARD Well, it should be pretty easy to flush you out. A simple question or two.

EDDIE Don't make me laugh.

EDWARD Well, answer me this, then, go on, answer me this! Where . . . no, wait . . . when . . . yes, yes, this is it! When is my birthday?

EDDIE Your birthday? How shou —

EDWARD Yes, my birthday. Edward Lane's birthday. If you are Edward Lane, as you claim, it shouldn't be too much trouble for you.

EDDIE No, you tell me.

Pause.

EDWARD Pardon?

EDDIE You . . . tell . . . me. Easy as that.

EDWARD But, but I —

EDDIE If you know your birthday, tell me.

EDWARD Look —

EDDIE You're the one who thinks he's Eddie Lane. I know who I am. And like you said, Edward the first and Edward the second. I was first.

Pause.

EDWARD First, in that you were here first, in the café.

EDDIE Right.

EDWARD But not necessarily that you're Edward Lane.

EDDIE Oh —

EDWARD No, I took your word on that.

EDDIE What do you mean, you took my bloody word?

EDWARD I did! I believed you! But I think I was a bit too trusting, too open —

EDDIE Too trusting!

EDWARD Yes, and now you're confirming my suspicions. You're doing everything you can to avoid my simple, straightforward question. You're being evasive —

EDDIE All right, all right, all right! My birthday, *my* birthday, is the fifteenth of March.

EDWARD My God. You have been checking up on me. You know my birthday! Why are you doing this?

EDDIE What —

EDWARD What do you want?

EDDIE *(Scornful)* What do you mean, what do I want? 'Course I know my own bloody birthday!

EDWARD OK, OK! Another question! One more!

EDDIE Tell me why the hell I should answer any —

EDWARD One more! One more! *(Pause.)* What was . . . I know, I know! What was the road my family lived in when I was born?

EDDIE Ha.

EDWARD Tell me! What road! Tell me!

EDDIE *(Defiant.)* Well, I don't know about you, but the road *I* lived in was O'Connor Avenue.

EDWARD Wha — you *know*!

The WAITRESS *has heard the commotion, and enters left. She approaches the table.*

WAITRESS Um, excuse me, but do you think you could keep the noise down? The other customers can hardly hear themselves think. *(*EDDIE *and* EDWARD *both look at her, and both subside a little, albeit reluctantly. She goes to clear more dishes from another table.)* Thank you.

EDWARD *(Hissing)* How do you know?

EDDIE What do you mean, how do I know?

EDWARD Just that — how do you know all about *me*? About me, Edward Lane? *(The* WAITRESS *passes by again, pausing by the table to give* EDWARD *a warning look. He quietens down. She exits left.)* Yes, she's right. I should keep quiet. You know too much already.

Pause.

EDDIE Wait a minute. I come in here for a quiet read of the paper, and you come in, you sit down at my table, and you start telling me that you're me.

EDWARD I think I've said enough.

EDDIE No! Excuse me, but you've come in here and all but accused me of lying! *(EDWARD says nothing.)* You can't just sit there, and . . . and pretend nothing's happened!

EDWARD You're in no position to tell me what I can and can't do.

EDDIE Look, I can — no, *I'm going to* prove that *I* am the real Eddie Lane, and you . . . well, God knows who you are. But I'm going to find you out!

EDWARD I'm telling you nothing more.

EDDIE What! I answered your —

EDWARD You frighten me.

EDDIE *I frighten you!* That's rich —

EDWARD I don't know how you know such private things about me. You've been snooping somehow.

EDDIE I've been . . . bloody hell! *(Stands, then looks up towards the WAITRESS, off-stage, and thinks better of it. He sits.)* How dare you accuse me of snooping! You make me sound like a Peeping Tom or something. What right have you got to make accusations like that? You've only known me — ha! *Known* me! If you can call it that! — you've only known me for five minutes, and you accuse me of lying to you, of not being who I am, of pretending to be you, of frightening you, and, and, and now you say I've been snooping! How bloody dare you! *I* am Eddie Lane, and I demand you —

EDWARD *(Calm but firm.)* You'll demand nothing. *(Pause.* EDDIE *is speechless with frustration.)* What you're doing is at best deceitful, and at worst it's a criminal offence. *(Pause.)* I could call the police.

Pause.

EDDIE Go on, then, call them. Call the bloody police.

EDWARD Oh, you'd like that, wouldn't you? Is that what you're after? An embarrassing scene, where the police cart us both off to check our credentials? *(Pause.)* That's it, isn't it? You want to humiliate me in public! In my own home town!

EDDIE Oh, please.

EDWARD And if I called the police, you know what the outcome would be, don't you? *(Pause.)* Don't you?

EDDIE You must want to be me really badly.

EDWARD Answer me!

EDDIE You want to be me really badly, don't you?

EDWARD What? Don't be —

EDDIE Well, OK, go on, then. *(Pause.)* Be me.

Pause.

EDWARD Be you —

EDDIE Be Eddie Lane. Be Edward Lane. It's all the same. Be me.

EDWARD Are you saying —

EDDIE I'm saying you can. I'm letting you.

EDWARD And, and . . . I —

EDDIE Well?

EDWARD *(Getting a grip)* Are you admitting you're not Edward Lane?

EDDIE Did I say that?

EDWARD You implied it.

EDDIE No —

EDWARD Yes!

EDDIE I said —

EDWARD That I am Edward Lane! Thus, *you* aren't!

EDDIE Don't, don't put words —

EDWARD People like you are dangerous. You're a public menace. *(Pause.)* You need help.

EDDIE *I* need help?

EDWARD Yes. You do. Listening to you just now, I wondered what it is that makes you do it, that makes you need *to be* someone else. You do, I can see it in you. You need to be someone else. It's very sad. I thought maybe you'd read too many glossy magazines and you wanted to be the Marlboro man or something. *(Pause.)* But I don't think you've got enough imagination. And you certainly haven't got the looks. No, you know what I think it is? *(EDDIE looks up defensively, as if perhaps there's a grain of truth in EDWARD's accusation.)* You want to know? Do you? *(Pause.)* Cat got your tongue? Ha! I've got you all worked out, and you're scared!

EDDIE Look —

EDWARD Don't wriggle. Don't try and slip out of it. I've got you, and I'm going to tell you what I know about you.

EDDIE What?

Pause.

EDWARD You're inadequate. Insecure. Your life adds up to nothing, and you make up for it by masquerading as other people, more glamourous, exciting people, people who've done something with their lives, people who *do*, who *achieve*, who *fulfil*, people who *are. (Pause.)* People like me.

EDDIE I —

EDWARD *(Excited.)* And I know why you chose me. Well, I'm pretty sure. You saw me — I don't know where or when, but you saw me somewhere — and you were jealous. Jealous! Mind you, it's perfectly understandable. I love this place, this town, but I've got a life outside it. Friends. I travel. If I want to do something, I do it. There's no barrier, no reason I shouldn't do all the things I want to in life. I *can*. But you . . . you can't. It's obvious — look at you! Is it confidence? Poverty? Are you depressed or unstable or something? It's something, though, isn't it? I can tell. It's something, all right. *(Pause.)* You're disappointed in yourself, disappointed in how you've turned out. You had hopes and dreams when you were younger, fantasies about what you'd do and who you'd be. You'd be someone. A film star. A doctor. A ship's captain. What was it, eh? You wanted to be rich, and you're not? You wanted women to flock to you, and they don't? Come on, what was it? What was it?! Tell me! *(Pause.)* You've failed, haven't you, at everything you've tried, so you looked around for somebody with a life, and you found me. My bad luck, I suppose. But not my bad luck that my life amounts to something, to all the things you dreamed yours would be, that my life *is* everything your life *isn't*, that I've succeeded everywhere you've failed. *(Pause.)* You've sunk so low, it proves you're no Edward Lane. No one worthy of the name could amount to so little, could be so pathetic, so abject. *(Pause.)* Have you had children? *(EDDIE looks up, but says nothing.)* Have you? I'm sure you — no, you don't look capable. Had any treatment for it? They can do wonders for impotent men these days. Probably the root of all your troubles, your need to pretend —

EDDIE I'm not . . . I'm not impotent.

EDWARD Don't —

EDDIE I'm not . . . I'm —

EDWARD *(Stands up, walks round to stand over* EDDIE.*)* How dare you! You come in here and try to sully my name! To ruin my life! How dare you! *(Pause, then menacing:)* I want my name back. I want you to admit you're not Edward Lane. I want to hear you say it. Are you listening? Are you listening to me? I want to hear you say it. "I am not Edward Lane." I want to hear you say it. *(Pause.* EDDIE *twists to look up at* EDWARD.*)* CAN YOU HEAR ME? Say it. Go on. "I am not Edward Lane." *(Pause.)* Go on. Say it. SAY IT! DO YOU HEAR ME? SAY IT!

EDDIE I . . . no, no . . . I'm not —

EDWARD *(Screaming.)* GET OUT! GET OUT, YOU IMPOS-TOR! HOW DARE YOU PRETEND TO BE ME! YOU'RE NOT FIT TO SPEAK THE NAME "EDWARD LANE"! GET OUT! GET OUT!

> *As he yells, he drives* EDDIE *from the café. One or two chairs get knocked over as* EDDIE *flees, which brings the* WAITRESS *on stage. She rushes over to pick up the chair(s), while* EDWARD *straightens his clothes and looks indignantly out after* EDDIE.

WAITRESS He's gone, then, has he?

EDWARD Yes. Yes, I think it's safe to say that.

> EDWARD *walks back to his place at the table. He sits down and smiles amiably at her.*

WAITRESS It was a bit noisy. I . . . I was afraid to come out.

EDWARD Yes. Noisy. Look, I'm sorry for the disturbance, only I don't think he's very well. Not feeling himself.

The WAITRESS *comes to* EDWARD's *table to pick up* EDDIE's *teapot, etc.*

WAITRESS Well. He didn't even pay.

The bell jangles again, and the door shuts. EDWARD *and the* WAITRESS *look across. The* WAITRESS *deposits* EDDIE's *teapot and so on on the uncleared table and crosses to meet the* MAN *who has just entered.*

WAITRESS Just one?

MAN *(Surveys the busy café.)* Yes. But is there —

EDWARD There's room here, if you don't mind sharing.

The WAITRESS *looks at the* MAN.

MAN Er . . . no. *(Crosses to* EDWARD's *table.)* No, that's kind of you. *(Sits down.)* Thanks.

EDWARD Oh, my pleasure . . . my pleasure entirely.

Tableau: EDWARD, *smiling; the* MAN, *looking at the menu left on the table; and the* WAITRESS, *looking across at the two of them. Blackout.*

The Regurgitator

MIRANDA YATES

Miranda Yates is 24 years old; she has been writing poetry and short stories ever since she first learnt to tell lies. She is currently working on a novel about impotence, the Odyssey *and a failed author of self-help books.*

One

Whatever a regurgitator swallows comes back out the same way. Nothing he consumes can ever touch or alter him. And he cannot transform it himself. He is no magician. This is only the slightest sleight of mouth — no doves, just a quick swallow. This is a gurning of the gullet; more of a damp biological squib than a magic trick. His handkerchieves are for blowing his nose.

The regurgitator has lived on both sides of the street. Odd and even numbers; lanes, groves and closes; streets named after trees and left-wing politicians; roads that revive dead wives and cul-de-sacs that clip the wings of birds. You can cobble their names together to make great American hero-narrators: Freeman Finch-Heath or Garth Eagles-Coppice; boys who grew up too fast and felt yearnings, just like the regurgitator, only with more eloquence.

The regurgitator has lived in places where you held your nose on the landing. He has been in homes where children ran under cars and sniffed rubbish, while the cats stayed in all afternoon to watch soap operas and cried at bathtime. He has stayed in town houses where, like real wild ones, they wrapped Christmas lights around their plants and stocked their toilets with saucy books and road signs.

He has camped in a stone doorway with steps running up the front and sides like a four-poster bed for a masochist. The pillars stood tall, like four impossibly cold and imposing waiters bearing stone grapes and naked piping angels in great bowls high above their heads. Here he spouted red-stripe poetry, clear as a stone cherub: "There's no double glazing in the windows of the soul, sweetheart."

"Listen mate, show me a family man and I'll show you a traveller who's cut off his feet."

Here he lay motionless on his left-hand side and, like a miracle statue, passed water as he slept.

The first thing he regurgitated was a pair of square black-rimmed glasses, that looked like minature TV screens. They belonged to his foster-father, Samuel, who called himself Uncle Bob because he was a kind man but not kind enough to let the fact pass unnoticed. You only have to ask and Bob's your uncle. Uncle Bob had a startling habit of suddenly rearing into people's faces and whinnying: "Good! Good idea, Sonny Jim!" ten minutes after it had ceased to be appropriate to a conversation. The regurgitator used to think that Uncle Bob was perpetually distracted from day-to-day happenings, by the shows running so close to his face on the two screens. Uncle Bob even described his day, like the *Radio Times:* "At 9.00 — a visit to the Post Office had strange and unexpected consequences. New drama about that missing parcel. 10.00 — went to the bank. A half-hour repeat of Tuesday afternoon's performance."

Once, when Uncle Bob was helping the regurgitator with his home-work (and wearing his smile like a ticklish plaster, because secretly he found patiently acknowledging the needs of a disadvantaged child, who might otherwise slip through the academic net, was piss boring), he took off his glasses, arm by arm, and placed them upright on the mantelpiece.

His face closed in on the regurgitator's and beamed with all its teeth.

"Time to take a break," he informed him. "Going to the shops. Then we'll be discussing your sums and lots, lots more. Back soon, don't go away." He tapped his glasses and said they would be watching the regurgitator, to make sure he wasn't getting up to any 'naughties'.

The regurgitator was at that dull, heavily documented stage in childhood when you thought too much about words. By 'naughties' Uncle Bob meant poking scraps of orange peel between the bars of the gas fire or hiding the glass sea lion in intrepid places. 'Naughties' did not include swallowing and regurgitating spectacles.

First the regurgitator folded the arms of the glasses, threw back his head, lowered them into his throat, and swallowed. Next he crossed his legs and put his finger to his lips because he imagined that the glasses were recording his movements like security screens and he wanted to be good. When they began to tickle his throat, he made a back-to-front swallow (the same as the one for manufacturing burps), wiped them dry on his cardigan and returned them to the mantelpiece.

The second time he regurgitated was in the children's home, where they half-drew the hairy purple curtains and hid in window ledges from each other. Some of them set alarm clocks so they could spook themselves at midnight and sneak about, filching kitchen knives and toothbrushes. The regurgitator would make pretend snoring noises, smack his lips and let them poke a comb in his mouth so it looked like a cigarette. One night the soft, luminous hands of his newest sister crept in circles on his back, sweeping him to sleep. In this house he swallowed a stolen kinetic-scientific-calculator-diver's watch with an alarm that played Yankee Doodle Dandy. He brought it back up in bed, using its small green light to work out how many times he would be on washing-up, on vacuuming, on laundry, on first sitting for breakfast, if he lived up to threescore years and ten. And how long he had been here altogether; in months, in days, in hours, in minutes, in seconds.

When he was older he regurgitated rings and strings of beads to impress girls. Some tucked in their chins and shot him withering looks as if vomiting jewellery was just so bloody typical for a boy. The best ones laughed and took their damp necklaces quietly from his hands, as if they were medals that they wanted to wear but did not believe they had quite deserved.

Two

The regurgitator's memory has grown up into a big wide-boy: very flashy; thin yellow teeth like a heap of matchsticks; always on his nerves, in his face, round his house. It squeezes him in a bare hug and does him over and over, so he chunders small talk and puppet shows. He heaves love letters, hairstyles and ants' nests. He barfs drying paint and ditch-water, cities written on strips of cardboard box and prides of Red Lions. He spews last summer's ferns smouldering on an embankment, and the head of a man he once saw, without a body, crying blood on the hard shoulder.

In quiet moments, he thinks, "Ah well, better out than in."
But there are not many of these moments.
He keeps an open bottle of white wine by the phone and calls up women in the afternoon. Next to the wine there's a stack of holiday brochures. With his left hand as a paddle, he can drift away from the thick clouds of gabble into empty skies.

He makes his living eating fire on the streets and sighing it all out like a dragon who would rather be a knight or even a lady.

His flat has more stairs than living space. He is always climbing, up and down, down and up. Making life difficult for himself.
Even having a crap is a great effort. He's perpetually constipated, though he scatters dried figs on his muesli and drinks a full *cafétière* at breakfast.
He is a regurgitator, it takes him forever to digest things.

It is taking him forever to digest his past. One tragic purple moment.

He thinks he understands purple. Most thoughts are grey, but some are purple. He has some ideas about the power of purple. He suspects that purple is exalted, born to reign over us, to tax us, to set us rioting, to plunder our best-laid plans, to whip our asses. Purple can have us painting pictures or offering up the fussy little delicacies of our lives on a plate. He knows that he wears purple,

himself, as an everyday overcoat, even though it doesn't keep out
the cold and he ought, really, to be saving it for best. He believes you
can remove purple stains with a bit of elbow-grease or a sprinkle of
household salt. One day it will all come out in the wash.

Three

This is the regurgitator's purple moment.

It is raining. It is dawning. Mother and son walk towards us. He
is the only boy in the world and she is the only girl. Nothing will
ever matter in the same old way. You can tell the little regurgitator
doesn't know this because he dangles from her hand, his feet
skimming the ground like a kite given too little slack to lift off. Her
umbrella blows inside-out. She throws it at a dustbin, without waiting to see where it lands. She is made of the city — you can see it in
her face. You can tell she speaks dry rot, and will grow up clutching
at walls. You can tell that her head and her heart are ten paces from
each other and although it will be a dirty fight, her head was always
going to be the winner.

He is lost in her city, her borders and perimeters. She is the town-
crier, the mayor, the architect, the highest steeple, and the
crap-stained lift to the bottom floor. He is just a small boy. She
paints his pictures, she picks his clothes and lays them on his bed,
for him to choose from.

She gives him a fireman's lift up the steps. "Hup we go!" The tiles
in the porch are dry triangles, red and purple. The doorbells are
living on top of each other. They both look poor. His anorak is a
nylon wafer. She does his top popper, rough as she can. Her eyes
find their way towards his. Click and fasten.

Mother: Be a good boy . . .
Son: Nope.
Mother: Wait in here for me until I get back.
Son: *(Shaking his whole body to indicate . . .)* Nope.

Then she walks away, carrying his birthday and both her names and the last one of his with her.

She looks back just once, over her shoulder. Her hair is wet. In her face you can feel his asking and something crueller and more elegant than any of the purple words he might have found for it, and nothing else is there.

Four

Some afternoons when the weather looks wet or unpromising, the regurgitator drinks black coffee. The café is well chosen; it smells of chick-peas and rolling tobacco, and there are lots of unnecessary corners. It is popular with tired people and those who like to think they've 'found' somewhere. The staff go out together in the evening, flirt sleepily with one another and drink apple tea all day until you say you want something. At night dim streetlights grope the wall where someone painted a naive penis and explained beneath how to use it. People come here when the public toilets are closed or to take each other fitfully on the way back from a nearby theatre.

They like him in the café, because he is an irregular regular who tips without expecting to find out the first names of the staff or how they spent their weekends.

Fair's fair then. The women are his own business.

The regurgitator wipes condensation from the window with his coat sleeve. He looks for long hair and no umbrella.

He looks until their eyes click and fasten. Then he waves just once with a flat hand, as if he is lifting up the old air like a blind. One she or another will climb the steps into the porch, shivering, beads of rain in her long hair.

From then on, it depends on the woman. She might sit first then speak, or speak then sit, or those choices may not even be there to be made. They might stand face to face like statues that have known one another for eternity but never touched, or kiss like train carriages locked on the same inevitable journey. One woman once stood in the doorway, knelt, clapped her hands and opened her arms as wide as the world.

In their own ways, they all felt sure they had known him before; perhaps in the moment when their eyes twitter between sleeping and waking.

For every woman convinced that the regurgitator has been searching for her, there is another who sees his face and believes she has found what she has always been looking for. Those who were more purple of temperament than grey suspected they were not alone in this familiarity that ached and thrilled like a once-broken bone.

When he takes them home, it always goes the same way. He throws open the window by his bed and tosses her gently onto her front. She turns to look at him over her shoulder, trying to catch the baby words that run like the rain from his purple tongue. She goes in and comes out the same way — early in the morning in a warm damp coat. Nothing has touched or altered her. She knew all along that it would be like this.

Five

One afternoon the regurgitator found he could still smell last night's stand on his sheets. He paced his carpets, feeling on his bare feet the warm queasy patches directly above the pipes, and the rough part where he had once cut a piece of Blu-Tack from the pile. He had a bad cough and felt bunged up. She had not moulted a single hair, he noticed.

"Actually, I pride myself on being, you know, together," she had told him.

Yet, he thought, there was something incomplete about her. Shamelessly, indecently, she had exposed a sort of absence. She even looked unfinished. She was thin and frail; all nipple and no breast; all leg and no hip. There were two insinuating bumps above her eyes but no eyebrows and no upper eyelashes. This had given her eyes a constant look of startled arousal; out-of-the-blue blue, fresh-woken confusion. He imagined her mother in the last throes of labour, panting between her legs: "I hope you're not intending to come out into the cold wearing just that flimsy thing, young lady. Back inside and dress yourself in something decent."

Even the manner they met was incomplete. They missed out a couple of vital stages and botched the order, so it was a rushed job and he felt ashamed about their shoddy workmanship. She was already inside the café when he arrived. Her hair was short and dry; her wet umbrella propped against her chair, its long steel point marking the polished floor. He heard the waiter saying: "So, so, but knackering . . ." She must have asked him about his weekend. Despite these anomalies, he never doubted that she was that afternoon's night in.

Her lips bloomed over the hot rim of the coffee cup, but she made no pleasantries. He was slightly stroppy and distracted because she wanted them both to leave before he could order his usual coffee.

It began to rain; he tried to open the window but found it was jammed. She lay on her front in the bed and sniffed his pillows.

"Would you throw me out of bed for eating a cracker?" she asked.

He said, "Never, ever," but she was not satisfied until he brought her a water biscuit on a saucer. Then she sat up, with the quilt tucked over her breasts, and licked off the butter, holding the plate under her chin to catch crumbs.

When they made love she said things he couldn't quite take in.

"Come on, son. Catch up. Chop, chop. Do you want me to leave you behind, eh? What would you do if I left you there?"

As he came, she tugged on his hand and turned to look at him over her shoulder with mild, distracted affection.

She left at dawn when the air was the colour of an ancient bruise. He pretended to sleep. The bed vibrated as she sat down to tie up her shoelaces. With his eyes closed he heard her tiptoe from room to room, humming and sucking her lip. Occasionally she stopped dead in her tracks. She opened the front door and must have stood there like a coat-stand for a minute, at least, before she closed it gently behind her. When she had gone he lay on his back and watched the battered light turn feeble white, and heal without a scar.

Six

The evening after his afternoon of pacing, he hand-washed his sheets and regurgitated her stutters, sniffs and bitten lips; the moments when her voice dipped to and from him, clogging through the strands of hair that tended to fall across his ears. He regurgitated the acoustics of moving traffic, a car boot opening, and the inscrutable pause of a panting dog outside his window.

The following morning she was waiting on the doorstep with the milk bottles, her hair a nest of stiff blonde beaks, pecking at the sky. She glided up the stairs gracefully, with her shoulders back as if she was being pulled on a rope.

"I think I left something behind," she told him, peeping through the kitchen door. She began to pull off the settee cushions and pile them up on the floor. Then she dived under his bed, shaking out his old shoes and paper backs. His hands felt dithery and too free, so he threw open his wardrobe and began to lay hands on his clean shirts, throwing the hangers one by one over his shoulder, to amuse her.

She stood with her hands on her hips, blowing her fringe up, for a moment.

"I think it's purple we're looking for. Something beginning with purple and ending in, I don't know . . . grey?" she murmured.

"Pppppp . . ." he said, as he emptied his paper rack.

"Pppppp . . ." she said, as she threw out the drawers of his freezer.

"Pppppp . . ." he said, as he pulled his towels from the airing cupboard.

"Pppppp . . ." she said, as she poured a mountain of All Bran on the kitchen table.

311

"Pppppp . . ." they said, as they rolled back the carpets, as they lifted pictures from his walls, as they took teaspoons and dug up the dry soil of his cactus plants, as they tore off the wallpaper with palate knives, as ragged violets fell through the air, bedding down on the floorboards, as if it was springtime in this stray and frangible world.

"Pppppp . . ." as they prised the floorboards loose with a crowbar.

They sat outside on the the doorstep at dawn, when they had given up the search, and the foam that came out of the settee cushions got on her lungs, and he felt queasy, either at the sight of the goldfish swimming in a half-pint glass or the smell on his hands from the little pebbles at the bottom of its tank.

She sang hits from musicals and made-up love songs to him, godless hymns that soared and opened up to white squall and to nothing, like elevators travelling through space.

And she was patient as the regurgitator held her hand to the gathering light and scratched out her splinters with his thumbnail.

If it was all right with him, she said she would wait here until the missing purple returned, intact, as these things tended to, either the moment you stop looking, or the moment you stop reminding yourself that you've stopped looking.

The regurgitator rubbed his mouth and tried to swallow her words. The missing purple had become lodged deep in his gullet and he was half-afraid that it would choke him. But he kept this to himself, because he knew what he thought now would never come back out the same way. It was bound to touch or alter him.

Instead, he told her there was something in his throat, a kind of plug or a lump.

"Say 'Aaah'," she said, and he gagged while she held down his tongue with her smallest finger.

Charterhouse Library

83965